INDUSTRIAL AND COMMERCIAL ESTATES
PLANNING AND SITE DEVELOPMENT

INDUSTRIAL AND COMMERCIAL ESTATES
PLANNING AND SITE DEVELOPMENT

English Estates, Scottish Development Agency, Welsh
Development Agency, Industrial Development Board
of Northern Ireland, Development Board for Rural Wales,
and the Highlands and Islands Development Board

 Thomas Telford, London

Published by Thomas Telford Limited, Telford House, P.O. Box 101,
26–34 Old Street, London EC1P 1JH, England

First published 1986

D
624
I N D

British Library Cataloguing in Publication Data:

Planning and site development : industrial and commercial estates.
1. Building sites
I. English Estates
624   TH375

ISBN: 0 7277 0263 7

Printed in Great Britain by Billing and Sons Ltd, Worcester

FOREWORD

Six agencies of central government - English Estates, the Scottish Development Agency, the Welsh Development Agency, the Industrial Development Board of Northern Ireland, the Development Board for Rural Wales and the Highlands & Islands Development Board, provide prepared and serviced land for industrial and commercial development in their regions. These organisations are referred to collectively as the 'development agencies' throughout the guide. Buildings are provided on a speculative or custom-built basis either by the appropriate agency or by private developers.

The whole operation is a significant part of the Government's activity in encouraging economic development in the United Kingdom. The efficiency and effectiveness of the work is therefore an important area of study. A working party of senior officers of the development agencies was formed to identify the key factors in site selection, planning and development. In addition, these technical activities were to be reviewed against the background of the commercial aspects of development.

The remit of the working party was set out as follows:

- Estate planning and site development includes the identification, appraisal and selection of sites for industrial and commercial development and their preparation and services ready for building

- The study is to examine the process of site planning and development. It will establish guidelines for cost-effective design and construction.

Its members were:

C D MacCalman [Chairman] : formerly Principal Civil Engineer, Scottish Development Agency

R C Bennett, Regional Manager, English Estates

R Griffiths, Board Engineer, Development Board for Rural Wales

J W Hall, Engineering Consultant, English Estates

D H Mann, Head of Design, Scottish Development Agency

J H Pavitt, Director Operational Planning, Welsh Development Agency

V H Skyrme, Chief Civil Engineer, Welsh Development Agency

M W Stevenson, Senior Engineer, Industrial Development Board, Northern Ireland

Many other members of the staffs of the agencies have contributed to the study. In addition there have been extensive consultations with local authorities, public utility undertakings, consultants, contractors, new town development corporations and other government agencies.

The working party extends its thanks to all those who have helped it in its work.

CONTENTS

INTRODUCTION

The purpose of this guide is to encourage an effective approach to the development of industrial and commercial estates.

The guide covers the planning and site development of estates with emphasis on projects carried out in advance of identified building requirements. In particular, 'Planning and site development' gives guidance towards fulfilling the needs of modern estates. It has been structured to stress the essential need for the integration of both commercial and technical aspects of any development.

'Planning and site development' draws from the considerable experience of the participating development agencies located throughout the United Kingdom in order to create a better understanding of the technicalities of estate development. This experience started in the 1930s, when the first estates were created. From those early days, the Development Agencies now own 7.8 million sq m [84 million sq ft] of factory space and 4,400 hectares [11,000 acres] of developed and serviced land. These figures do not include many successful sales of property to the private sector and apply to March 1985.

Based on this specialised knowledge, the guide provides a framework for the essential judgements and decisions required for successful projects. This framework is explained under four main headings in the guide.

- THE DEVELOPMENT PROCESS
- ASSESSMENT
- PLANNING AND DESIGN
- IMPLEMENTATION

Development Process

The logic of the development sequence is set out at the beginning of the guide. A haphazard and uncoordinated approach can rarely hope to survive through the many pitfalls of development. The guide therefore starts with the developer setting out his objectives and follows the process through to the final product of buildings or availability of serviced land. Emphasis is placed on the importance of measuring and achieving the developer's financial objectives.

1

Introduction

Assessment

This guide points out the need for thorough technical assessment of the site at the initial stages of the development process. Correct procedures and practice for topographical surveys and ground investigations are identified because of their significance to building costs. It is also made clear that without consideration of these basic items, the success of any project cannot be accurately predicted.

Planning and Design

Estate planning described in the guide involves logical use of available information in order to plan an estate to the maximum effect. Successful estate planning and site development can only be achieved on the basis of teamwork coupled with an understanding of the development process. Inadequate planning or design can have a serious impact on the buildings in terms of cost, commercial success and viability.

The character of commercial and industrial estates is changing, not least because of new technologies being developed. These changes are resulting in more sophisticated developments with different standards, demands on public utilities, densities of development and landscape policies.

Planning and design of the landscape structure is examined against this background of change. Importance is placed on its contribution to the marketability of a site, together with the need to plan for future maintenance.

Considerable experience has been built up over many years on the technical requirements for highways, public utilities and drainage. A national survey was carried out to provide a sound basis on which to predict road traffic generation. Research within the development agencies allowed more accurate consumption figures for public utilities to be put forward. The chapters covering these topics recommend standards suitable for industrial and commercial estates.

Implementation

'Planning and site development' stresses that fundamental decisions are needed to establish the programme of site works and discusses the merits and difficulties of advance site preparation. Carrying out site development works in advance of building has proved successful with the authors in terms of programme and costs, and advice is given on basic points which have to be borne in mind when proceeding with a number of separate contracts concurrently.

Finally, a word of warning. The topics are closely interrelated and care should be taken to avoid reading one chapter out of context with the others.

THE DEVELOPMENT PROCESS

Chapter 1

THE DEVELOPMENT PROCESS — AN OVERVIEW

INTRODUCTION

The development process in relation to estate planning and site
development spans a sequence of events from identification of a demand
or need to develop to the realisation of the development potential of
the selected area in accordance with predetermined objectives. A
model progression of events is presented which highlights the
different facets of the development process from site selection
through to the implementation of the site development scheme itself.

The separate stages will vary, merge and change sequence in practice
as each individual site and scheme is unique. This chapter indicates
to professional teams how they should coordinate the elements of the
process and keep the developer informed.

The term "Developer" is used to defined the decision maker and funding
source and covers large public organisations down to individuals.

The developer's objectives are largely dictated by the nature of the
developer itself. The "commercial" objective involves the primary aim
of creating profit by means of sales or rentals. Economic or social
objectives of government or local agencies are primarily designed to
benefit a country, region or community through the provision of
industrial or commercial land. The objectives are not mutually
exclusive. Decisions on viability should be taken in the light of
normal commercial criteria to ensure the most cost effective
implementation of any particular scheme.

LOCATION AND SITE IDENTIFICATION

An initial decision has to be taken by a developer about the area
within which it wishes to build. This decision will depend on the
nature of the developer and in particular its development goals. It
could be looking at a wide geographical area or it could be site
specific.

Identify demand

The stimulating factor behind any decision to develop will normally be
the commercial judgement that a demand exists for a product in a

particular area. Where no commercial motives exist, the development may have social/economic objectives, but site identification should still take account of the following criteria.

A full analysis of enquiries received over a one or two year period by all private and public sources should be made to assess demand for the range of industrial or commercial opportunities under consideration. In addition, recent sales and lettings should be analysed over a similar period to assess the conversions from enquiries to occupations.

Cross-referencing these results against the supply of land/accommodation already on the market, and that coming onto the market, should identify gaps where obvious enquiries are not being satisfied.

Confirm demand

Having identified areas of demand, these could be confirmed by undertaking direct target market research exercises into live enquiries and into other companies throughout the country whom it is considered may be attracted to the locality.

This exercise could be undertaken by in-house market research personnel, or by expert external companies who would operate to a specific brief.

Where the developer is following strictly social/economic objectives, it is likely to be considering areas where enquiries are very limited and market analysis unreliable due to lack of comparables. In these instances the decision to develop is often based on the premise that estate provision would attract demand that would otherwise not be apparent.

Site search

Having identified demand or perceived demand, a range of locations have to be considered to house the proposed estate. A number of factors have to be assessed in relation to each site viewed, and the compatibility of the site in relation to these factors will ultimately provide a "short-list" of probabilities, as is shown under the following headings

- Rental Demand
- Usage
- Local Factors
- Planning
- Site Boundaries
- Future requirements

Rental demand

Existing or projected rental and sales levels are a major factor in location decisions, higher levels being normally achieved where demand is healthy for a particular product.

The consideration of comparable rental evidence from various areas influences developers´ locational preference towards certain areas and away from others. If there is not a market history then professional judgement is required on projected rental and sale levels to determine the acceptability of a location. Even at this preliminary stage the developer will take an overview as to the likelihood of achieving its required profit/rate of return. This overview would take account of likely costs based on schemes of a similar nature. If it seems that the minimum return based on optimum costs and rents cannot be achieved then alternative locations may have to be considered. In a commercial sense some locations would be disregarded at an early stage subject to any appropriate non-commercial factors. The medium of rent expresses the relative advantages/disadvantages of any particular location and is a significant factor. Nevertheless other considerations have to be taken into account.

Usage

As a result of the demand identification exercise detailed above, the requirements of potential users should be considered in relation to acceptable locations and matters, such as communications, market and labour proximity and environment. Differing types of industry obviously have different requirements when considering their ´ideal´ site.

Estate uses can be categorised as follows:

- Light industry
- General industry
- Special industry
- Wholesale warehousing
- Retail warehousing [cash and carry]
- High technology uses - research, development, production
- Offices
- Land suited for occupiers to build to their own requirements
- Land suited to speculative building
- Land required for future schemes [land bank].

Consideration should be given to the following criteria when the range of site uses has been identified, and each location assessed in the light of predicted requirements.

- Accessibility to communication networks
- Proximity to work force
- Proximity to other related/compatible industry
- Proximity of product market for distribution, or essential suppliers of raw materials
- Requirements for abnormal accommodation, for example, substantial parking

Development process

- Proximity to surrounding environment where bad neighbour uses envisaged
- Competition from other users/estates in the proximity

Local factors

Local demand influences must also be taken into account where particular areas are considered attractive or substantially unpopular to the local business community, whether it be due to the quality of work force available, security or vandalism problems, or other factors.

Planning

The availability of existing outline planning permission or detailed permission could restrict the number of sites to be investigated. Consultation with the local planning authority is essential, not only to clarify existing zonings but also to determine where possible change of use may be considered. An outline planning application may be submitted, even where land is not appropriately zoned and consideration given to a subsequent appeal if refused. Planning and other requirements are considered in more detail in Chapter six under the heading 'Statutory Controls'.

Site boundaries

The general shape, topography and surroundings of the site should be studied as these may be a limiting factor for certain locations. Awkwardly shaped sites may well lend themselves to small unit accommodation, whereas larger units may not economically be sited where there are irregular boundaries with subsequent "dead" areas. Natural features may also make economic layouts difficult.

Future requirements

If the development is to take place in phases over a long-term the immediate development proposals should be planned and take into account likely future use.

The process of identifying an ideal site involves a considerable amount of market research within the area being considered. Sources of information on land availability are local authorities, government departments, statutory bodies or the private sector [for example, estate agents, development companies, organisations with substantial land holdings and so on].

Ultimately, one particular location will be selected as the most appropriate for the project or scheme proposed. In certain circumstances, two or even more locations may have comparable attractions, in which case these other options may be carried forward

to the preliminary appraisal stage. The cost of further detailed
investigations means that it is best to keep options to a minimum.

PRELIMINARY APPRAISAL

A preliminary appraisal is now required to determine whether in
principal the site selected can be physically and economically
developed to sustain the proposals envisaged. Any conclusions at this
stage will be subjected to re-evaluation at a later date but this
preliminary appraisal is essential in order to justify expenditure on
more detailed investigations which will follow in the next step of the
development process.

This stage usually denotes the technical appraisal process described
in Chapter three and the start of the estate planning process
described in Chapter six. These two processes will normally develop
over preliminary appraisal, feasibility study, and pre-contract
development programme stages, although early consideration will be
required, particularly in respect of some basic estate planning
matters.

An overview from the developer's point of view is given here detailing
the requirements at this stage of the brief to the consultants, and
the content of the ultimate report. The chapters referred to above
detail the technical appraisals and considerations undertaken on
behalf of the developer.

The developer will select a team of technical consultants which
according to circumstances would include engineers, architects,
surveyors, with particular expertise and experience in the type of
development to be undertaken. The developer must provide a clear
brief to this technical team who will be responsible for providing the
information and recommendations to the developer so that a decision on
viability can be taken. The fee basis of such a study must be agreed
with the technical team prior to start of the work in order to suit
the developer's budget. This may vary from the consultants doing this
study on a speculative basis to a full fee payable, irrespective of
whether the project ultimately proceeds or not. At the preliminary
appraisal stage it is usual for certain matters which may prejudice
the proposals to be cleared before incurring significant fees. These
could include planning principles and any legal conditions which may
relate to the land, and could be investigated by the developer or its
agent. The availability of the land at an acceptable purchase price
should also be confirmed.

Where nominations to the professional team are by way of in-house
appointments, the comments regarding fee structuring, are to some
extent, irrelevant. But the notional cost of in-house resources,
committed to a project which may prove abortive due to lack of early
enquiries, should never be disregarded.

The technical team would normally undertake the formalities of the
technical assessment and the many facets of estate planning. In the

case of large projects team members would co-ordinate small specialised teams for this function who would then report back to the 'lead' team whose responsibility it would be to co-ordinate reports and recommendations at all stages to the developer.

The brief at this stage should include details of:

- The site [sites] to be considered with name, address, location and contact points for owner, to enable access to be gained if necessary. A location plan should be attached.

- Proposed site requirements:

> Total size of scheme immediately proposed
> Details of treatment and option required
> for remainder of site [if any] including
> preferred plot sizes
>
> Details of identified site uses
>
> Specific sizes or range of sizes for
> buildings required, with proportions of
> each [if any]
>
> Density requirements for initial and
> further phases of development if
> appropriate
>
> Details of any expansion potential
> required for initial or future development
>
> Basic details of building construction,
> such as, single or multi-storey.

- Known restrictions or abnormalities from initial site search which may be pertinent to appraisal, such as, easements, rights of way, and so on.

- Deadlines for reports from the technical team.

- Request for indicative development layouts for the proposed scheme if required.

The wording for the brief should be as specific as possible in order to avoid irrelevant investigations into proposals not envisaged.

Where the land to be investigated is to be acquired for land bank purposes, a wider range of development layouts for potential uses will be required. In this case a merging of actions under preliminary and feasibility stages may well occur, in order to assess the overall potential. An indication of envisaged future development possibilities should be given where possible.

10

The time-scale for preparation of a preliminary report varies depending on the site being investigated. Two to six weeks should be adequate under normal circumstances.

The report should make specific recommendations about what detailed investigations are required to enable a clearer picture to be gained at feasibility study stage.

The preliminary appraisal stage is now completed by examining the original brief with the report findings. It must be confirmed that the plots or units envisaged can be provided within the site boundaries and that the resulting layout gives acceptable standard of space, road layout, common areas and complies acceptably in all other respects. Site abnormalities must be evaluated and the viability of developing difficult areas within the site assessed. Cost implications must be examined.

Where indicative figures reveal an uneconomic or unacceptable costly development, either measures must be taken to reduce costs, the proposed scheme must be abandoned, or the brief should be reviewed [if acceptable] in accordance with a more economic solution. If the site or sites meet the brief the next stage involving site selection is carried out.

SITE SELECTION

After the preliminary study has been evaluated, a decision whether to proceed or not to detailed feasibility stage is now made. If two or more sites are under consideration then selection must take place on the basis of which would provide the most acceptable scheme.

FEASIBILITY STUDY

The developer must now give a more detailed brief to the technical team to enable accurate estimated costings to be provided for the site selected.

All aspects of the site require evaluation and the costings and information accumulated during the feasibility study are needed so that a decision can be made to proceed to tender.

The technical team may now be broadened to include quantity surveyors and other specialist consultants required to assess methodology and estimated costings. The basis of fees should be considered again at this stage, where appropriate.

Detailed considerations under this study are identified again in Chapters three and six, and will encompass both technical appraisal and estate planning matters. The objective of this section, however, is to indicate what information will be required from the developer and the nature of the report back.

The comprehensive brief provided by the developer should particularly identify items which will involve additional costs such as a full ground investigation and topographical survey. The brief should contain the following items:

- A request for a full ground investigation survey to be undertaken specifying areas of site for which results are needed. Full cost and structural implications of ground conditions will be required by the developer who will expect to give approval to the expenditure required for the survey. Cost limitations - if any - should be detailed.

- A request for a topographical survey if this is considered appropriate - again including cost limitations and the requirement that approval for expenditure is necessary.

- Specific details of site from the preliminary appraisal stage together with any up-dated information on rights of way, easements, restrictive covenants and so on which have become available through land acquisition enquiries.

- Identification of site area and layout which is to comprise the first phase of work including the extent of infrastructure deemed appropriate. Details should be given of likely building specification including types and sizes of units, external works and special requirements. The information required includes:
    - Types of units required - workshops, offices, single or multi storey
    - Preferred basic external materials required
    - Eaves height and internal heights required
    - Internal clear spans/floor areas
    - Imposed floor loadings to be achieved
    - Basic service requirements - including capacities and loadings where able to be identified
    - Any required external treatments, such as, heavy vehicle turning
    - Internal office requirements
    - Any special or abnormal structural requirements for particular users, such as, craneage facilities requiring additional foundations
    - Road and associated drainage requirements
    - Special landscaping requirements.

- A budget for capital expenditure within which the development objectives can be achieved.

- A request for details of service and local authority requirements, covering all existing easements for pipes, cables, wires and so on crossing the site together with known restrictions on development, such as land to either side of services to be maintained for access purposes. Details of easements and so on required to service the site under consideration must be identified at any early date to enable negotiations to take place for the appropriate rights. It should be borne in mind that routes of cables, and so on, required to service the site itself, which cross areas which will not be adopted, will also require easements or leases to enable the statutory undertakers legal rights to lay and maintain their apparatus. The services may also have to cross private land outside the curtilage of the developer's ownership and easements will be required with adjoining landowners. Locations for electricity substations/pumping stations, and so on, should be identified as soon as possible.

- Instructions on the phasing and layout of the estate development, particularly where land in excess of Phase one requirements exists. This should include identification of advanced preparation and servicing, together with size of envisaged developable plots and types of uses. Estimates for what would be considered abnormal site development works should be requested. These would relate to all operations over and above what would be considered a normal development process, including excessive site clearance, ground stabilisation and demolition. The resulting cost implications would have a significant bearing on land acquisition negotiations.

- Finally, within the brief should be a request for estimated costings to be derived from the feasibility study. These would normally show:

> Total building cost element [if appropriate]
> Abnormal site development costs
> Infrastructure costs not related to specified phases
> Fees - professional consultants, and so on
> Clerk of Works/supervision charges
> Administration charges [if any]
> Statutory charges [planning fees, road adoption fees]
> VAT or other tax elements
> Insurance

It is essential to have clearly defined the costing breakdown given above, with abnormal site conditions highlighted, giving estimated costings for each constituent part, a description of each particular problem encountered and recommendations for solutions. The costings for what would be considered abnormal site development, for example, excessive site clearance, ground stabilisation and demolitions are all operations which a tenant taking a development site on a serviced estate would not normally expect to encounter or fund.

Costing information is essential for provision of services, including foul and surface water drainage, electricty, gas, water and telecom. Estimates for all supplies to service the estate as a whole must be provided and these should give a breakdown of costs for distribution within the proposed estate, and costs of a capital nature to bring the supply onto the site in the first instance. Differentiation should also be made of facilities which will service

13

not only an initial phase, but also later phases, as costs in respect of these items may be dealt with on a proportionate basis when undertaking the detailed appraisal.

A time-scale for preparation of the report should be quoted in order to maintain a realistic programme. This will vary according to size and could be from six weeks to six months.

The full feasibility study when received should be comprehensive, clear and concise and must confirm that the brief has been met or identify any variations. Where possible, it should be presented in one document with attached plans.

Concurrent with the detailed technical feasibility study will run the developers own enquiries into land acquisition and legal matters as part of the initial enquiries to the land owner. It is useful for a preliminary questionnaire to be forwarded for the owner's comments, including the following points:

- Request for copy of deed plans to be forwarded
- Full names/addresses of owners/tenants/occupiers
- Particulars of interest held - freehold/leasehold
- Terms of any payments required
- Details of any restrictive or other covenants running with the title
- Is the sale with vacant possession or subject to tenancies? If the latter, details of terms will be required
- Details of easements, rights of way, services, sewers, or other restrictions or rights subsisting or to be imposed on the site
- Particulars of boundaries, fences and responsibilities
- Details of rights of support or light affecting property
- Particulars of any other special conditions
- Details of any titles, land tax or other charges on the property
- Particulars of existing access rights to highways and any associated rights and liabilities
- Details of existing planning permissions/applications pending
- Ownership details of mines and minerals
- Any leases or agreements in respect of minerals and so on.

The results of these enquiries will obviously have significant bearing on site development considerations and any valid factors which may be discovered during the course of enquiries should be made known to the technical team.

Having obtained information, costings and recommendations from both the detailed feasibility study and land enquiries, the developer must then look at the project as a whole and determine whether the original development objectives can be satisfactorily achieved, before proceeding to detailed design stage. The developer should satisfy itself that planning principles are agreed, legal and physical encumbrances are identified and capable of solution, and

14

that the land purchase negotiations are progressing to a satisfactory conclusion.

COMMERCIAL APPRAISAL

The first consideration is to establish whether or not the detailed brief has been achieved. Any variation from the brief must be examined and a decision given on the acceptability of the revisions in the light of demand indications and development objectives.

Assuming a project meets criteria and objectives, it will now be possible to undertake an appraisal on cost levels and profit/return. The techniques of commercial appraisals are discussed in detail in Chapter two.

The appraisal having been completed, a decision point is now required on the extent of works or first phase works to achieve the development objectives, yet keep within the overall return criteria. The feasibility study will detail site works required to prepare land ripe for development. Examples may be: ground stabilisation techniques to remedy poor subsoil conditions; land drainage installations to reduce the overall water table; service road construction to open up development potential; and service installations of appropriate length and capacity to cater for envisaged development. The level of expenditure to provide an acceptable return will be indicated by the appraisal and depending on the development objective of the developer, this will either indicate the maximun capital commitment, or the level of subsidy required to implement the proposals.

Once a decision to progress to tender, or otherwise, has been made, site acquisition negotiations should be carried out in unison to ensure consecutive dates for legal completion and start of building works. The timescale for agreeing legal documentation and precontract enquiries should not be under-estimated.

Detailed planning submissions and other approvals detailed in Chapter six should also be synchronised at this time in order to achieve a fully valid and acceptable permission which does not impose unacceptable limitations on the work on site.

PROJECT BRIEF

A decision to proceed means that the developer must formalise a detailed development project brief. This should contain an update of the developer's brief given at feasibility study stage, as appropriate, taking account of decisions made in the commercial appraisal and broadly including:

- Instructions to proceed
- Target costs limit and mechanism for cost updating

- Layout specification with plot size requirements
- Site details - up dated through land enquiries, and so on.
- Estate specification, for example, roads, services, landscaping, and so on.

The developer should ensure that it details any specific requirements it may have under the numerous elements of estate planning [see Chapter six].

A full building specification must be provided where a phase one scheme incorporates a building project within the development; and instruction must be given on the "use classes" required for the project within the formal planning application, which should also anticipate all future uses required.

The project brief must give instruction on future management and maintenance criteria. Unacceptable design detail and materials should be stipulated, together with acceptable items which through past management operations have proved successful. Consideration should particularly be given to the life expectancy of materials and cost-in-use criteria. The layout of the estate should conform with a planned management policy in terms of land upkeep, maintenance and repair, giving easily maintained areas at economic cost.

The purpose of this project brief is to ensure that the technical team are fully aware of the complete end product required by the developer. It may be that in drawing up the project brief the developer would seek the advice of various disciplines in the technical team on specific matters.

PRECONTRACT DEVELOPMENT PROGRAMME

A precontract programme must be prepared as the technical team proceeds with detailed design of the scheme, with periodic reference back to the developer for comment/approval. The programme should take account of lead-in times for consultation and response from statutory undertakers, meetings of planning committees and so on. A timetable of events for in-house approvals by the developer concerned should be built in and estimated dates for tenders and start of contract should be quoted. From this programme the developer will be able to assess its financial position and cash flow.

Estate planning is finalised at the detailed design stage by the development of approved outline proposals which are based on the criteria of Chapter six under the heading 'Elements of estate planning'. The detailed design stage may only cover some of the outline proposals but is set against the approved long-term strategy for the estate.

In all cases it is essential that the entire programme is continuously monitored and that the developer is told of any variations in the time-scale. Any amendments required by the developer or made necessary by site conditions or design criteria during the course of detailed design should be made known to all parties.

Prior to tender, the team will report on the proposals, together with implications for estate planning of the entire area to form the ultimate estate, to receive the developer's final approval. The overall estate development plan will include all aspects of highway provision [Chapter nine], drainage provision [Chapter 11], landscaping [Chapter seven], and public utilities [Chapter 10], in addition to the full estate planning criteria referred to above in Chapter six. It is crucial that the long-term plan is accepted prior to initiating early phases.

The developer is ultimately looking for recommendations from the technical team on the overall estate plan at the culmination of the precontract development programme, and that suitable tenders have then been received to implement the first phases of this strategy.

APPROVALS

After receipt of tenders, the technical team should satisfy itself that the lowest tender contains no errors. Then a report should be submitted to the developer giving a breakdown of received tenders, details of proposed contract programme and a recommendation about the tender to be accepted. Any divergence from previous assumptions on details of scheme, costings or contract period should be highlighted and reasons given for such differences. Significant cost implications must be explored and recommendations made. The report should also include details of planning permissions and conditions, building regulations and progress on road and sewer adoption agreements.

On receiving the report, the developer will compare recommended tender figures with estimates to confirm that rates of return or profit are still acceptable. Should this not be the case several options exist, for example:

- if tenders are below estimate, including additional items to increase attraction/lettability, or acceptance of lower cost and implicit higher return.

- if tenders exceed estimate, negotiation of tender details to amend the specification to give savings without reducing return; acceptance of increased costs and inherently lower return/profit margins; or cancellation of the scheme and acceptance of abortive costs.

On account of procedures for approvals after receipt of tenders, it is advisable to hold prices open for acceptance for 90 days, where possible.

IMPLEMENTATION

Signing of the site works/building contract can take up to three weeks and in the interim confirmation is needed that possession of the site has been finalised and that all statutory or other approvals and permissions have been obtained.

Monitoring of costings is essential during the period of the contract if fluctuations are allowed. Estimates of fluctuation levels will be needed by the developer so its capital commitments can be assessed.

Continual monitoring is required even assuming a fixed price contract. Any significant variations encountered on site should be referred to the developer with recommendations on action to enable a decision to be made. The spelling out of cost implications is essential.

Authority to sanction variations up to a certain limit may be delegated by the developer to the technical team. This should be clearly agreed.

Lastly, continual forecasting of cash payments is necessary to allow the developer to predict cash flow.

Chapter 2

COMMERCIAL APPRAISAL

As mentioned in Chapter one, several techniques are applied to determine the viability of a project in terms of either cost criteria, profit or loss calculations, or return to be achieved on capital employed.

As an initial consideration, it is assumed that the development to be appraised involves no associated building works. In that case the following elements require identification, using information supplied by the technical team, or information from the developer´s own resources.

Estimated total land acquisition price   )
Legal fees, duty on purchase price   )   Land
Costs of obtaining possession, compensation   )   Costs

Total site development costs [including roads,   )
services, levelling, landscaping, and so on]   )
Ground investigation/survey costs   )   Develop-
Design fees   )   ment
Statutory fees   )   Costs
Clerk of Works/inspections   )
Unrecoverable tax [VAT,etc]   )
Internal adminstration costs [if applicable]   )

Interest payments on:

- land for period until completion of development)
  contract   )

- proportion of development costs during period of)   Finance
  contract on basis of timing of stage payments   )   Costs

- full land and development costs during estimated)
  average period of vacancy from completion of   )
  contract to sale/lease   )

- agents fees for sales/lettings   )
  advertising/promotional costs   )   Other
  funding fees [if applicable]   )   Costs

In certain areas grants might be available to the developer in respect of specific works to be undertaken and these sums should be taken into account when calculating the anticipated return.

In a similar manner certain public bodies or agencies achieve development of difficult areas of land which would be unattractive to private developers by accepting a certain subsidy element in reclaiming and providing infrastructure works. An allowance for this subsidy should be clearly identified and taken into account in assessing the viability of a scheme.

If the serviced site is to be sold in plots on a capital basis then estimated capital value should be assessed in respect of fully serviced industrial or commercial land, ready for disposal. The appropriate figure will relate to appropriate possible uses, position of plot on the estate and the total area which will be practically released by construction of the infrastructure on a net developable basis.

The difference between total costs and total estimated capital receipts will provide a figure of profit or loss, against which the success of the project can be assessed. If on the other hand plots are to be leased on ground rents, it will be necessary to estimate ground rent for a fully serviced developable plot, again according to location and position within the estate.

The net rental income is then expressed as a proportion of total costs, and the return would be compared against normally accepted commercial criteria or a predetermined base in accordance with development objectives previously discussed.

An example of a hypothetical site development appraisal is given in Example A, Appendix one. All figures used in examples have been based upon imperial measurements which are currently still standard within the surveying profession for agency and investment valuation procedures. Principles would apply equally for metric measurements.

Initial site development works with an associated building scheme may take up fully the area under consideration. In this case additional costs need consideration as in Example B Appendix one, and the assessment of return on capital based on estimated rental income can be calculated. On the basis of a capital sale of the completed development, a profit/loss calculation is prepared.

Under certain circumstances, where a large site is being considered but only a proportion of it is to be developed as a first phase, site development works may open up more land than is required for the initial buildings. An apportionment of site development costings can therefore be attributed to later phases. An example of this is shown in Example C, Appendix one. The remaining serviced land would usually attract an enhanced value, and if sold would provide a profit or loss to the developer when compared with the total of site development costs and original acquisition figure.

Certain public agencies undertake development of difficult areas of land which would be unecommical to private developers. A certain subsidy element in reclamation, site development and infrastructure works might have to be accepted and from an accounting viewpoint, this can be readily identified from Example C.

Circumstances may also exist where other objectives take priority and override normal considerations. For example, budgetary time limits or tax considerations may encourage a level of expenditure at a particular time, over and above what would give acceptable returns. This could result in development objectives being revised.

Despite the individual requirements of any particular developer, the project should aim to maximise the relationship between costs and income through the most cost-effective scheme in the optimum location.

ASSESSMENT

Chapter 3

TECHNICAL ASSESSMENT OF POTENTIAL INDUSTRIAL AND COMMERCIAL SITES

INTRODUCTION

Sites which are both relatively easy to develop and available are becoming increasingly rare so difficult sites set aside in the past may now require close re-examination. Rigorous assessment techniques are essential to avoid serious financial and technical problems at a later stage when there is a commitment to develop.

That accepted, thorough investigation of a potential site should be regarded by the developer as a positive investment. Ground investigation and pertinent surveys enable best use of the site and ensure the best return on capital. A sound report also assists in land acquisition negotiations and determination of land price.

SITE ASSESSMENT

There are two methods of assessing potential sites: the preliminary appraisal, which is the more simple and provides a quick answer; and the more detailed feasibility study, designed to provide a thorough assessment of a site and to uncover likely problems.

The feasibility study can follow on from the preliminary appraisals but the extent of overlap and depth of assessment will be determined by each site. Details listed below of what is required give a clear indication of good practice.

Item	Preliminary appraisal	Feasibility study
Purpose	To provide a quick factual answer to the potential of site	To establish firm development options and technical feasibility of project
Name and Location	Name of site, ordnance survey grid reference and local authorities	Name of site, project name, ordnance survey grid reference and local authorities
Site area	Gross land area, Significant areas of water identified separately	Gross land area and net developable areas in detail calculated on the basis of legal boundaries, significant physical constraints and areas reserved for future development

Item	Preliminary appraisal	Feasibility study
Ownership and legal conditions	Name of owner, tenancies and other rights where known	Full details of owners, tenancies and rights together with future conditions relating to land. Additional legal conditions relating to easements, rights of servitude, wayleaves, bridle ways, public footpaths and rights of way
Planning status	Current planning status together with details of restrictions	Current planning status together with details of restrictions – tree preservation orders, for example, and history of previous applications
Use of site	Current and previous use	History of site in detail, including current use in order to identify future development problems from past usage
Ground conditions	Brief description of ground if known. Any available mineral reports should be attached	Full description of ground together with details of investigations into mineral, geological and subsoil conditions. Contamination of land should be mentioned. Report should be attached [if available] from the Mineral Valuer; National Coal Board; British Geological Survey; Geological Survey [Northern Ireland]; Health & Safety Executive Any restrictions to the development should be identified
Access	Identify present access to site, new access point and any possible difficulties where known	Detailed examination of road access to the site together with other forms of transport. Full examination of potential difficulties and general accessibility of the site,

Item	Preliminary appraisal	Feasibility study
		including proximity access of public transport, rail, shipping, aircraft for larger sites. Ownership and availability of land required for additional access, plus any necessary external road improvements
Drainage	Location and availability of foul, surface water and land drainage - with particular reference to availability of outfalls	Full details of existing foul sewers and availability of foul sewerage together with any identified restrictions such as trade effluent discharge. The need for special measures such as pumping and alterations to public sewage works should be highlighted. Location of surface water drains and water courses identified along with restriction of discharge of surface water and pollutions control aspects. Full details of existing land drainage and measures to improve the system as necessary. Special land drainage measures to improve ground conditions should be noted
Public utilities	Location and availability of electricity, gas, telecommunications and water together with any known limitations of supply and influence on development	Location of existing electricity, gas, telecommunications and water mains together with full details of availability of supplies. Limitations in terms of capacity, time scale and restrictions imposed by existing mains should be clearly detailed.
Private services	Location	Location of private apparatus - including cable television - together with details of rights

27

Item	Preliminary appraisal	Feasibility study
Topography	Brief description of site, including levels	Detailed visual description of site, identifying significant features such as water courses, mature landscaping and steep slopes. Detailed land survey required to aid assessment of developable potential and costs
Existing buildings	Brief description of condition of existing buildings	Full details of condition and potential reuse of buildings [possibly in a separate document which is summarised in the feasibility report] Details of proposed future developments on or adjacent to site
Boundaries	Not within scope of preliminary appraisal	Description of site boundaries and surrounding developments in particular reference to restrictions on proposed development. Potential neighbour problems should be identified, together with the need to support adjoining property. Existing boundaries formed by canals, railways and navigable rivers can impose limitations on development and the appropriate authorities should be consulted
Environment	Not within scope of preliminary appraisal	Air pollution, noise, and climate to be examined in detail. The effect of radar clearances and radio transmissions should be established together with any height restriction proximity of any major hazard site should be checked with Health & Safety Executive

Item	Preliminary appraisal	Feasibility study
Landscaping	Not within scope of preliminary appraisal	Detailed survey of existing landscape in order to provide information for new landscaping design and maintenance
Additional information	Brief description of any special points obvious from visual inspection such as flooding or undesirable adjacent developments	Further points of detail such as historic buildings, river or coastal defence work, retaining walls and bridges, flooding and comments from other organisations which may have an interest in the site
Proposed development	Not within scope of preliminary appraisal	Preparation and assessment of trial development layouts to arrive at the optimum design solution which complies with the commercial brief and is acceptable to the planning authority. The trial development layout will also confirm whether or not the commercial brief can be met; and identify areas for structural landscaping
Site preparation and servicing	Not within scope of preliminary appraisal	Measures necessary to prepare, access and service the site together with any phasing of works to suit the commercial brief
Cost of development	Not within scope of preliminary appraisal except in the broadest of cost ranges. Extraordinary site development costs should be identified, however, together with any features which might lead to higher than normal building costs	Detailed costing of proposed development including comparison with alternatives assessed on a unit cost basis. Costs of each phase of development should be listed where appropriate and abnormal building costs identified. Costs of site investigations and fees should be included.

Item	Preliminary appraisal	Feasibility study
Conclusion and recommend- ations	Identification and summary of significant technical factors and further assessment work required.	Positive recommendations regarding development of site based on the commercial brief and findings of the report should be highlighted and alternative plans suggested if appropriate
Time of Preparation	Two to six weeks	Six weeks to six months
Progress meetings	Generally not required	Three to four week intervals
Personnel	Senior staff generally from a civil/structural engineering background, with other specialist advice when necessary	Full team of professionals
Drawings	Simple site plan and location plan	Fully detailed drawings illustrating: - Location of site - Extent of site and its planning context, ownerships [including adjoining owners], rights and leases - Location of existing services and road access points - Existing topography - Development constraints, if applicable - Trial development layouts, including possible alternatives - Site preparation and servicing requirements, including phasing as appropriate - Identification of building phase, if appropriate

Drawings within the document could be to the following scales:

Site area	Scale
Up to 1 ha [2.5 ac]	— 1:500
1 ha – 10 ha [25 ac]	— 1:1250
10 ha and above	— 1:2500

For larger studies photographs, perspectives and models may also be required.

PRODUCTION OF REPORT

The objective of the report is to present in clear and concise terms the characteristics of the site under consideration for development, written in a formal way to ensure adequate status. It is essential that the commercial brief is clearly laid out in full to set the report in context; and that the preliminary appraisals should be in a simple format with increasingly higher standards for the feasibility studies, depending on size and sensitivity of developments under consideration.

Lengthy reports should be provided with a summary. If costs of the development are likely to be sensitive it is best for these to be detailed in a separate document.

All reports should have drawings bound into them and a maximum drawing size of A3 is advised; the drawings themselves should be kept relatively simple. It is perfectly practicable to provide separate appendices to the report containing detailed information, and these can include larger scale drawings.

Copies of correspondence with public utilities, mineral reports and planning consents, together with other relevant correspondence should either be bound into the back of the report or included in the separate appendix.

The credibility of a report rests on its accuracy. Text and contributions should be checked by the report team and contributors for errors and their accuracy verified by each individual involved.

As already mentioned the preliminary appraisal report can involve a preparation time from two to six weeks with feasibility studies taking anything from six weeks to six months. Delay by the developer in approving detailed ground investigations or surveys can prolong the report process. If a borehole investigation is needed it can take as long as 12 weeks for example.

Delays can sometimes be experienced in obtaining information from public utilities and local authorities, so contact must be made as early as possible. Approaches should be made to identified individuals in preference to general enquiries, if possible quoting consumption demand figures.

The preliminary appraisal type of report is best produced by senior staff with adequate experience to appreciate potential problems merely by visual inspection of the site. A civil engineer backed up by appropriate advice is best suited to produce a preliminary appraisal.

On the other hand, the feasibility study requires the appointment of a balanced team of professionals. A study leader, who might either be the developer's representative or a member of the professional team, should be identified at the start of any major assessment and made responsible for co-ordination of effort and final production of the report. A timetable should be agreed as well as a ceiling figure of costs for both fees and investigations, with both time-scale and costs kept under regular review.

It is unlikely that detailed interim reports will be required for preliminary appraisals because of the relatively short time-scale. But feasibility studies generally require considerable interaction with the developer and progress meetings are desirable at about three to four week intervals.

Chapter 4

TOPOGRAPHICAL SURVEYS

EXISTING INFORMATION

A proposed development area requires early identification in plan form. Initial plans in the UK can usually be provided by Ordnance Survey which is constantly updating its maps and frequently holds unpublished data known as SUSI [Supply Unissued Survey Information]. This is supplied on request only; an enlargement and reduction service carried out by private reproduction companies under licence is also available through OS.

There are central government libraries of photography undertaken by aerial survey contractors. Reference can be made to these libraries throughout the UK and can provide useful historical information from the Second World War onwards. Aerial photographs have a stereoscopic application and ´oblique´ photographs can be used for marketing or planning a site.

Little progress, even at sketch plan stage, can be made without reliable survey information. An immediate commitment of funds is needed to cover the cost of survey work and other types of initial investigation.

NEED FOR TOPOGRAPHICAL SURVEY

The survey provides a precise definition of the development area to an appropriate scale incorporating all the physical features including variation in levels, boundary fences, adjacent land and buildings with their relative levels, roads, sewers, public utilities landscape features and water courses. This information is necessary to design, measure and construct the project as well as forming a base for any legal documents, site investigation reports and so on.

GUIDANCE ON SURVEY WORK

Surveys are usually let to specialist survey contractors. A wide range of techniques is available and the decision on which to use can be left with the survey contractor although particular methods known to be inadequate for the specified degree of accuracy might be specifically precluded by the design team. Time and cost must come into the reckoning and there are some advantages in the design team itself undertaking the survey - not least the saving of time and retention of site information. At the very least the team should carry out a ground check on work done by outside specialists.

The minimum survey scale adopted should be 1:500 with a possibility of 1:200 for smaller sites. All survey plans should have a small scale location key plan and sufficient detail must be taken to enable specific areas of the site to be plotted to a larger scale, depending on requirements. Levels should be shown on plan as spot levels or contours with survey control stations including a confirmed ordnance bench mark clearly indicated on drawings and the survey itself aligned with the national grid.

The tender documents for a survey can follow the normal format of construction tenders. Of particular importance is the need to specify the limits of accuracy of the survey and whether or not a digital ground model [for automatic plotting] is required. Information on the means of gaining access to the site should be given to tenderers. Research has shown it is not possible to generalise about survey costs as each site requires individual assessment.

PREPARATION OF BRIEF

The developer's brief to the design team should confirm that right of entry has been obtained and identify contacts. Indication should also be provided of the extent of survey, budget costs and programme.

Following the analysis of tender prices for survey work, it was concluded that it would be misleading to provide a cost guide £/hectare owing to the varied nature of the individual sites, for instance, shape, topography, dense vegetation, building intensity. Specialist advice should be sought when preparing a survey budget for a complex site.

Chapter 5

GROUND INVESTIGATION

INTRODUCTION

Identification of ground conditions at the site is essential to a
proposed development. This is possible to a limited extent by careful
consideration of local geological records and other existing reference
sources. But usually additional investigative work has to be carried
out on site.

Early priority must be given to ground investigation by the design
team as little progress can be made on the design of the development
without this information. This means an immediate commitment to
preliminary costs to cover ground investigation which may range from
a minimal amount to a substantial figure, dependent upon the
complexity of the geology and the physical nature of the
investigation. Reference should be made at all times to the Code of
Practice for Site Investigation BS 5930 : 1981 [formerly CP 2001].

NEED FOR GEOLOGICAL/GROUND INFORMATION

Ground investigation enables the design team to:

- Assess the underlying geological structure, the
  possible disturbance thereof and its effect on the
  development surface including properties of superficial
  strata materials to aid foundation and other
  elements of design; including the need for ground
  improvement measures

- Identify the presence of contamination in the form
  of gases or other toxic materials and assess measures
  necessary to ensure safety both during and after
  completion of construction

- Identify the presence and possible variations in
  level of ground water - for both construction and
  post-construction reasons [for example, heat pumps]

- Prepare the design brief and contract specifications
  to embrace earthworks; slope stability; recompaction;

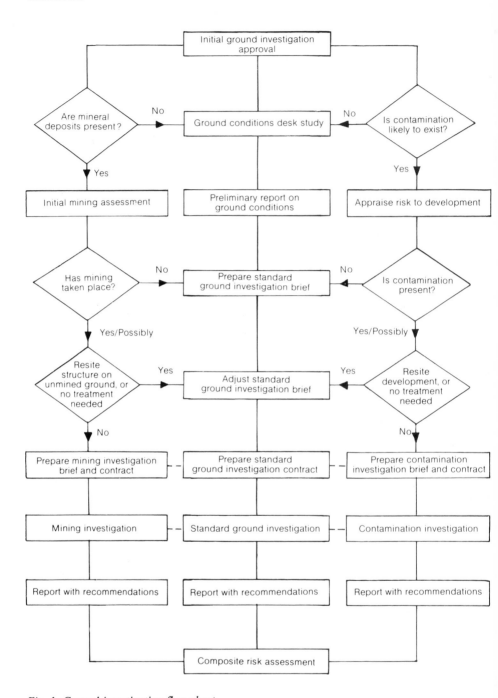

Fig. 1. Ground investigation flow chart

road and design; trenching and so on

- Identify the cost implications of site development
  and building construction.

PREPARATION OF BRIEF

The developer´s ground investigation brief to the design team should include:

- Confirmation of right of entry to the land and details
  of condition of entry

- Make available all previous information obtained during
  initial site appraisal, topographical surveys and desk
  studies

- Details of potential development, that is type of buildings,
  foundations/floor loadings and location of buildings.

- A budget cost recognising that curtailment of the design
  team´s ground information requirements can result in a
  qualified report

- A programme for execution of the works and provision of
  all the necessary reports including the carrying out of
  laboratory tests.

Assistance should be given by the technical team to prepare this brief.

It is then the technical team´s responsibility to provide in detail a brief to the ground investigation contractor by way of his contract documents, so that the necessary information is obtained to satisfy the developer´s brief.

IMPLEMENTATION OF GROUND INVESTIGATIONS

The implementation of a ground investigation consists of a number of activities which follow on one from the other. This is best illustrated in the ground investigation flow chart [see Fig. 1]. The first step is to carry out a desk study which entails a visual site inspection and examination of all records such as geological maps, aerial photographs and so on. The desk study will yield a preliminary report which will aid the preparation of the technical brief for the main ground investigation and assess the degree of risk associated with the site.

The techniques available for ground investigation in the field range through trial pitting, cable percussive drilling [shell and auger], rotary drilling, electrical penetrometer and geophysical methods such as resistivity. The selection or combination of these techniques will depend on the site.

Testing of soils can either be carried out by means of field measurement or by laboratory tests on carefully selected samples. The field tests involve measurement of the movement of ground water and strengths of the ground [see Appendix three].

The range of laboratory tests is extensive providing information on the type of soils and their likely behaviour together with their chemical properties. The type of tests to be selected depends very much on the material from the site and as this is not necessarily known in advance, frequently has to be left to the judgement of the engineer supervising the investigations.

Where the technical team has detailed expertise in the likely ground conditions it is practical to limit the contractor's responsibility to carrying out of the field work and provision of a factual report. The design team will provide the necessary interpretation of the results. However, in instances of complicated geological or subsoil conditions a specialist geotechnical engineer can be appointed whose responsibilities will be the interpretation of the results and the supervision of the contractor.

It is also possible that the contractor could provide an interpretative report but care is required if the design team has a follow-up design responsibility. It must be borne in mind that there are a limited number of geotechnical contractors who have the necessary capabilities of carrying out the large-scale ground investigations and producing comprehensive and interpretative reports. Large tender lists are not likely to be appropriate in these circumstances.

The ground investigation contract documents are generally based on the ICE Conditions of Contract or more specifically those for Ground investigation. They should specify the methods of investigation and scope of laboratory work envisaged. Contract drawings should also be provided showing details of boreholes and trial pits together with location of known public utilities. It is essential to examine the tenderer's insurance policies in respect of third party liability and so on in order to provide the necessary protection to the developer. A tender period of three weeks is normally allowed.

Small and straightforward ground investigation work can be carried out as either term contracts or annual tenders. This can take the form of a schedule of rates applied to notional quantities to provide a comparison of tender.

When the ground investigation has started in the field a tight control of cost is essential in order to avoid over-running the developer's budget. Ground investigation can be open ended in its nature and the driller's daily logs must be closely monitored. This control has to be balanced against the vital need to ensure that adequate information is collected for future design work so that repeat investigations are not required at a later date. Research has found the varied nature of the geology of an individual site makes generalisation of ground investigation costs impractical.

REPORTS

There are two forms of report which can be provided:

- The factual report provides a full description of the site, its geology and subsoils. It provides results of all laboratory and in situ tests and the factual information obtained from them.

- The interpretative/analytical report is an extension to the factual report. It deals with the interpretation of the results and the likely geological influence on the development. This report must also provide for the developer recommendations and conclusions on the nature of the ground conditions on the site and their implication on future design on a quantitative basis.

REFERENCES AND FURTHER READING

CLAYTON C.R.I., SIMONS N.E. and MATTHEWS M.C. Site investigation handbook for engineers. Department of Civil Engineering, University of Surrey. Granada Publishing Ltd – Technical Books Division, Frogmore, St Albans, Herts. First published in Great Britain 1982.

ROBB, A.D. ICE works construction guides – site investigation. Thomas Telford Limited, London, 1982.

PLANNING AND DESIGN

Chapter 6

ESTATE PLANNING

INTRODUCTION

The appointments made by a developer to a technical team for the
planning of an estate depend on the scale of the project and its
particular requirements. The team should always include a development
surveyor, an architect/planner and a civil engineer. In addition
specialist advice on landscaping and building costs may also be
required. Various arrangements of team members are likely at the
planning stage, involving combinations of the developer's staff,
consultants or contractors. It is essential however that a team
leader is identified at the outset and given the necessary authority
to manage the project.

This chapter describes the matters to be considered by a technical
team during the preparation of proposals for implementation. They are
discussed in the sequence in which they are generally considered but
the circumstances of each project will demand an appropriate plan of
work. Planning may be spread over a number of stages set out in
Chapter one - preliminary appraisal, feasibility study, project brief
and precontract development programme - or it may be concentrated into
the last and make use of the conclusions of earlier stages. It is
important that the plan of work ensures that every relevant item is
considered and that earlier conclusions are checked for continuing
validity.

OBTAINING AND ANALYSING INFORMATION

The technical team has to obtain and examine the following information
in order to develop a proposal or proposals for consideration by the
developer:

- The commercial brief for the development
- The developer's broader goals for his business
- The impact of planning and environmental controls
  on the development
- Particular constraints and opportunities associated
  within the particular site.

Commercial Brief

As explained in Chapter one the commercial brief can be very specific
or it can allow the technical team to develop a variety of options

within broad guidelines. However it is prepared, the brief should tell the team what is required, clearly specifying

- The planning work required [for example, an outline plan, a detailed report or site development or building proposals]

- The type of use to be attracted [for example, light, general or special industry, warehousing, research and development or offices] and the proportions of each type

- The type of development required [for example, speculative building by the developer, building to order or building by occupiers] and the proportions of each type

- The character of development required [for example, quality, density of development, single or mixed uses]

- The facilities required [for example, for transport, services, amenity-use and estate management]

- Design requirements to suit the proposed management plan [for example, freehold or leasehold sites, reservation of expansion areas, adoption of infrastructure and open space by public authorities

- The developer's arrangements for maintenance].

Developer's goals

However specific the brief, it is necessary for the team to understand the developer's broader business goals which affect its plan. A private developer may be primarily concerned with a particular level of profit or with building up the capital value of its portfolio of properties; whereas a public or local authority's prime objective may be the general economic benefit to a nation or a locality. In every case the team has to achieve an acceptable relationship between the quality and costs of development and the value of the product bearing in mind whether the developer intends to sell quickly or retain the estate. The source of development funds [for instance, retained profits, institutional funds, government grants or loans or international aid] comes into the equation, as do tax liabilities. The developer may also have an interest in a particular industrial sector or market area.

Statutory controls

The impact of statutory planning and environmental controls must be assessed. Planning consents which are based on the acceptability of development proposals are granted under conditions which define permitted uses generally by reference to statutory use classes. Consents may influence character of development [by controlling

density, areas reserved for amenity or landscape, building form and
materials, colours and signs] and control access from public highways.
They are often worded to prevent development that will increase
hazards and reduce detrimental effects on neighbours. The development
control system should also protect the estate against subsequent
detrimental development on adjacent sites.

Circulars issued by the appropriate government departments lay down
guidelines for planning authorities and should be studied by those
advising developers. Negotiation or appeal can sometimes vary
conditions imposed by authorities. In particular planning authorities
have been advised not to attempt to enforce controls which are the
subject of other regulations through planning conditions.

Environmental regulations are defined in legislation and statutory
instruments and administered by designated authorities. They
include:

- Health and safety regulations

- Regulations governing water, electricity and gas supplies
  and telecommunications services

- The Pipelines Act governing underground services

- Regulations for fire prevention and escape and access
  for fire fighting

- Control of pollution

- Highway and sewerage design standards

- Land drainage requirements in England, Wales and
  Northern Ireland and river purification requirements
  in Scotland

- Civil aviation regulations.

There may also be other constraints in the form of private and public
rights over land, local Acts of Parliament and covenants.

Site constraints and opportunities

The technical team must acquire a detailed knowledge of the site.
Ordnance surveys, reports of previous site appraisals, site visits,
ground level and aerial photographs, sketches and models are among
aids which should be used so that constraints and opportunities can be
identified and analysed before plans are prepared. It is important to
establish the characteristics that make a site unique and show how
they can be exploited to create a distinctive development.

45

OBJECTIVES OF ESTATE PLANNING

The planning of the estate must satisfy the commercial brief and optimise the following objectives in order to promote the best possible development in both the short- and long-term:

- To increase the value of developed land
- To be adaptable to future changes in requirements
- To provide an attractive environment at all phases of development
- To relate satisfactorily to community needs
- To allow good estate management

Increasing value

The value of developed land can be enhanced by careful location of different land uses. Prominent large sites can be provided for national and international companies or for higher value commercial uses such as retail distribution or offices. Bad neighbours can be sited away from main frontages. Direct and easy access to principal sites, improving the environment to reduce the effect of poor surroundings while enhancing natural features and converting as much of the site area as possible into attractive building floorspace all maximise a site's value. One other important factor to consider is phasing development so as to maximise the return from completed infrastructure.

Adaptability

Adaptability is necessary to meet changes in industrial processes which require different forms of plant, buildings and site layout, and economic priorities between different sectors of industry and within these sectors. Social changes such as the move to private cars away from public transport and attitudes over environmental issues can influence an estate's development, as can government policies and priorities. So a development plan should provide basic infrastructure which encourages mixed uses and does not inhibit variations in subdivision as development proceeds. It is sound policy to include buildings which are inherently adaptable. Space should be left for existing premises to expand with areas held in reserve for new occupiers.

The technical team should attempt to analyse change over a period agreed with the developer. The most effective provision is space to accommodate change - in particular the consistent trend towards a reduction in building density. This may be slowing down as new technology is introduced but it is unlikely to be reversed.

Environment

Providing an attractive environment at all phases of a development which may extend over 10 or 20 years is difficult if space is to be retained for the extension of premises. It is important to create an impression of a complete development, perhaps by building up street frontages and locating extension areas on back land with reserved access routes that allow for alternative uses.

Community needs

Positive measures to obtain local support can enhance the success of a new development. These may include the provision of screening and buffer zones to protect neighbours, sympathetic routing of traffic, agreement over reasonable noise levels with the local authority and provision of facilities that benefit locals as well as newcomers.

In some cases beneficial proposals will be accepted as 'planning gain' by local authorities. This may help towards the granting of planning consent.

Estate management

Management of the estate can be eased by planning landscaped areas that are sufficiently large and regular for economical maintenance; providing refuse storage to suit local collection and disposal arrangements; and providing service routes that are easily accessible to statutory undertakers for maintenance. A clear definition of intended plot boundaries helps, as does designing roads and sewers to ensure the level of adoption required by the developer.

ELEMENTS OF ESTATE PLANNING

The elements described below are common to most commercial and industrial estates and need to be considered by the planning team.

Land use

The developer will wish to convert as much of the gross site area as possible into developable plots suitable for lease or sale with or without buildings. How much will be released and how much will be retained by the developer will depend on management policy.

The size and shape of development plots play a large part in determining the layout of roads and their associated footways and public utility service reserves. Amenity areas, tree screens, estate facilities, water features and so on must be located to maximise the number of regular, well proportioned plots.

Table 1

Type of industrial activity	Floor area per employee			Floor space as % of net developable area [5]			Employees per net developable hectare [5]		
	Rural m²	Urban m²	All sites m²	Low %	High %	Typical %	Rural/ Low	Urban/ High	All sites/ Typical
Warehousing, wholesale, distribution [1]	77.4	41.7	59.5	35	50	40	45	120	67
Metals, manufacturing, vehicles	62.8	33.8	48.3	30	40	35	48	118	72
Chemicals, pharmaceuticals	57.3	30.9	44.1	30	40	35	52	129	79
Other manufacturing [3]	56.4	30.4	43.4	30	40	35	53	132	81
Transport	44.9	24.2	34.5	30	40	35	67	165	101
Food, drink, tobacco	43.2	23.2	33.2	30	40	35	69	172	105
Professional administration [2]	36.7	19.7	28.2	35	45	40	95	228	142
Instruments, electrical	35.6	19.2	27.4	30	40	35	84	208	128
Textiles, clothing	32.9	17.7	25.3	30	40	35	91	226	138
All types	51.8	27.4	40.0	30	40	35	58	146	88

Notes:
1. Includes SIC22 (distributive trades) and all warehousing, wholesale and retail premises related to other SIC groups.
2. Includes SIC23-27 inclusive and all research and administrative premises relating to SIC groups.
3. Includes paper and printing, bricks and glass, timber and furniture and construction.
4. All other groups include both manufacturing and servicing activities for the specified trades.
5. For definition of net developable area see paragraph 6.78.

Sources: Floor areas per employee – Industrial and Commercial Estate Traffic Generation part 2: Procedures for estimating Traffic Generation: paragraph 3.4, page 10.

Floorspace per net developable area – estimated for this report.

Employment

A developer will need to make some estimate of employment likely to be
generated by its estate in order to plan the site. In the initial
stages the developer is likely to consider employment in relation to
developable areas. At later stages it will be able to use the
building floor space but even after completion actual numbers employed
will vary greatly.

In Table 1, an attempt has been made to indicate likely employment
densities from data gathered during a survey of traffic generation.
A total of 58 estates containing 972 firms were included in the
survey and these were classified into nine types of industrial
activity. These types were derived from information on the standard
industrial classification for each firm, details of the type of
activity carried on within particular premises, and the number
employed.

The data indicated that employment densities may vary from 45-230
per hectare depending on industrial activity, location and layout.
If the developer cannot forecast the type of activity it would be
advisable to make an estimate of about 60 employees per hectare for
rural sites, increasing to 150 for an urban location; 83 being the
mean estimate for a typical development density [that is ratio of
floor space to developable area] of 35%. If the developer can
anticipate a bias towards a particular activity it will be possible
to refine the estimate.

Building form and development plots

Most modern industrial and storage uses favour a single floor level
whatever their size. Larger office and laboratory uses need at least
750 m2 [8000 sq ft] at each level. External areas for goods vehicles
need to be on a similar level to the ground floor or at a suitable
height for dock loading. Car parking areas, although not so closely
tied to the building, will require a relatively flat area for
economical layout.

Plots therefore need to be reasonably flat or easily graded. If the
levels vary on the site it will be necessary to grade plots of
appropriate size. Their dimensions will determine the economic
spacing of roads and service routes.

There is a considerable range of different forms of development.
Figs 2 - 4 and Table 2 illustrate options ranging from groups of
workshop units to free standing units of up to 5000sq m.

Fig. 2 applies to industrial estate layouts constrained by site
conditions and cost targets as it is economical in site development
works. It is also popular with small firms as the grouping of
entrances eases the problems of supervision for a small management

staff but tends to be untidy in practice as there is no provision for outside storage of materials or of refuse. The maximum plot size is limited by the relatively unimposing concentration of entrances on the main frontage.

This layout type is also sometimes used for small groups of retail premises where the relatively infrequent servicing movements are acceptable across the forecourt areas used by customers. It is not generally suitable for office buildings although it may occasionally be found on congested urban sites.

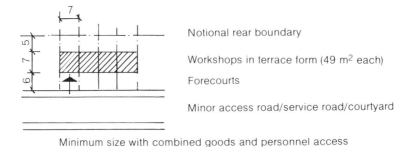

Notional rear boundary

Workshops in terrace form (49 m² each)

Forecourts

Minor access road/service road/courtyard

Minimum size with combined goods and personnel access

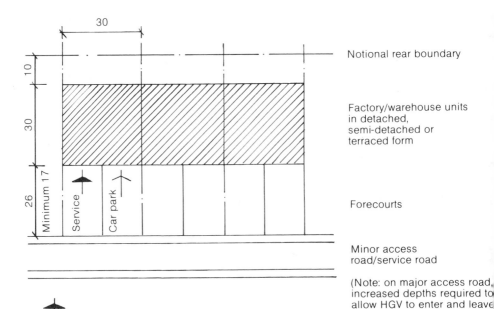

Notional rear boundary

Factory/warehouse units in detached, semi-detached or terraced form

Forecourts

Minor access road/service road

(Note: on major access road, increased depths required to allow HGV to enter and leave in a forward direction on local distributor roads, this layout form is unlikely to be acceptable because of frequency of access.)

Goods access

Personnel access

Fig. 2. Building layout — Type A (all dimensions in metres)

The layout in Fig. 3 is used to separate the service areas of industrial and commercial buildings from the personnel entrance or entrances provided for customers, management and staff. Apart from the increased cost for some form of rear service road, its principal disadvantages are the need for a relatively deep level site and more extended security arrangements. The main advantages are a more attractive "front door", a better environment for office work and the containment of service areas.

Units can be detached or semi-detached but the most general application is for parallel terraces or for more complex blocks

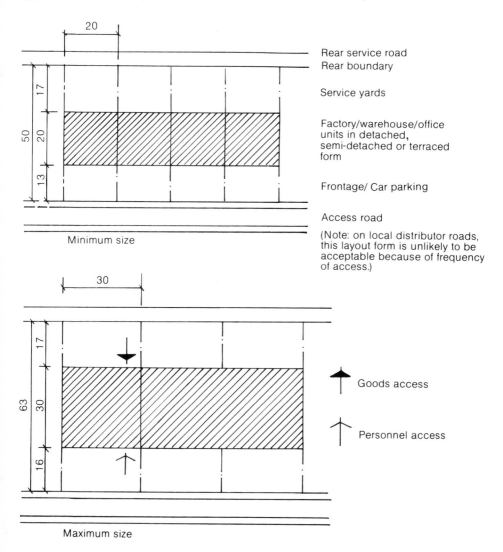

Fig. 3. Building layout — Type B (all dimensions in metres)

wrapped around a central service area. Units within terraces or blocks are unlikely to exceed 900sq m ground floor area unless allowance can be made for later extension.

Rear servicing may be applicable to offices and buildings for research and development activities.

The arrangement in Fig. 4 also separates the goods and personnel accesses but reduces the cost of site development by placing them on adjacent faces of the building. Extension to the rear is easier than for Fig. 2 or 3 as the service area can expand with the building. On

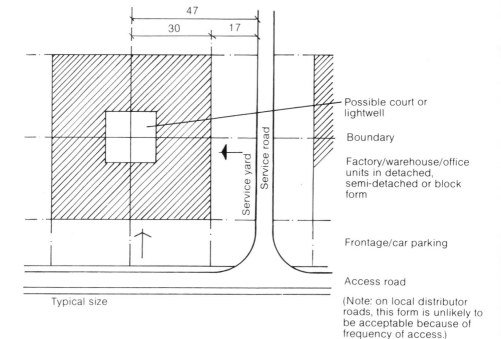

Possible court or lightwell

Boundary

Factory/warehouse/office units in detached, semi-detached or block form

Frontage/car parking

Access road

Typical size

(Note: on local distributor roads, this form is unlikely to be acceptable because of frequency of access.)

(Note: maximum size is likely to be limited by internal environmental requirements for units, and by the length of fire escape routes.)

Alternatively, service accesses could be on an access road with car parking and personnel access between buildings.

Goods access

Personnel access

Fig. 4. Building layout — Type C (all dimensions in metres)

52

industrial estates the service area could face the access road with offices fronting a landscaped car park between buildings.

This layout would be uneconomical for units with a ground floor area of less than about 500sq m. In block form units of more than 900sq m are unlikely to be attractive but larger units could be provided in detached or semi-detached form with provision for later extension.

The arrangement in Fig. 4 is suitable for most industrial and commercial uses.

A fourth arrangement [Type D in Table 2] is only applicable to detached premises set back from the plot boundaries on all sides. Personnel and service accesses can be located on any face and service goods and car parks freely disposed to suit. The density of development must be relatively low and this type is unlikely to be used for buildings of less than 900sq m ground floor area. For the present consideration an upper limit of 5000sq m has been assumed but much larger buildings are possible in the configuration.

Access systems

The design of roads and footpaths is dealt with in detail in Chapter nine but the implications of road traffic and pedestrian movement need to be considered as a major element of estate planning.

Access should be gained at the highest possible level in the urban or rural road hierarchy but only the largest estates will be allowed direct access from a motorway or trunk road junction. More usually the estate will be entered from district distributor roads which in turn access onto the trunk road and motorway systems. One access is sufficient for smaller sites but those exceeding 20 ha should have additional access. Where this is not possible consideration must be given to an alternative means of entry for emergency vehicles - either a separate controlled access or possibly a section of dual carriageway at the estate entrance.

A simple hierarchy of roads is required to convey traffic from the estate entrance to individual premises. The normal criteria used by highway authorities need to be extended and the following definitions have been adopted:

- Local Distributor Roads   to distribute traffic to different zones within the estate: limited frontage access

- Major Access Roads   with frequent frontage accesses to premises but with sufficient space inside plots to allow all movements on and off the road to be in a forward direction.

Table 2. Building layout types

Type	Description	Likely range of dimensions		Plot area (m²)	Ground floor area per unit (m²)	% ground floor area to plot area (m²)
		Frontage (m)	Depth(m)			
A	Access on one face of building only	7-30	18-66	126-1980	49-900	39-45
B	Personnel access on face: goods access on opposite face	20-30	50-63	1000-1890	200-5000	40-48
C	Personnel access on one face: goods access on adjacent face	40-87	39-140	1560-21280	500-5000	32-41
D	Personnel and goods accesses on all faces of building	70-130	70-130	4900-16900	900-5000	18-30

Note: In this table, plot area is measured within the curtilage. The percentages shown do not indicate the efficiency of utilisation of developable land within an estate

– Minor Access Roads	serving a smaller number of premises so that closely-spaced accessses can be allowed with some reversing movements on the road
– Service Roads	serving a small group of premises with a virtually open frontage and provision for manoeuvring on the road.

It is not essential that roads at all levels of the hierarchy are present in one estate, and alternatives are illustrated in Fig. 5. It should be remembered that a simple road layout is necessary to make it easy for visitors and delivery drivers to find their way to individual premises. They will be helped if there is a minimum number of turns between estate entrance and plot, and through roads or loops are used in preference to cul-de-sacs.

The footpath system has to be planned as carefully as the road system. Separate footpath systems are not recommended for most estates as they offer a lower level of security to pedestrians and to premises and are less convenient for random pedestrian movements. However, separate links to the urban footpath may be required as well as short cuts within the estate. Footpaths should be provided on both sides of the road where both sides are developed, but where plot entrances are very close, a defined footway may be provided flush with the road surface.

The road network should be designed to cater for public transport particularly if the site could provide a throughroute linking two external road systems together. Sites close to a passenger rail station and existing bus routes have obvious advantages.

Goods delivery and collection

There is little call for direct rail or canal access to estates but the possibility of these should not be ignored at the earliest stages of planning. Goods are normally transported by road and the layout should be capable of catering for large goods vehicles. It is often possible to attract a haulage firm to the estate to ensure good freight facilities are available.

Refuse storage and collection

There has been an enormous increase in the quantity of refuse generated in business premises and this now requires early consideration in estate planning. Refuse storage will normally be within the curtilage of the premises but the estate layout should take collection into account especially where small workshops share storage facilities.

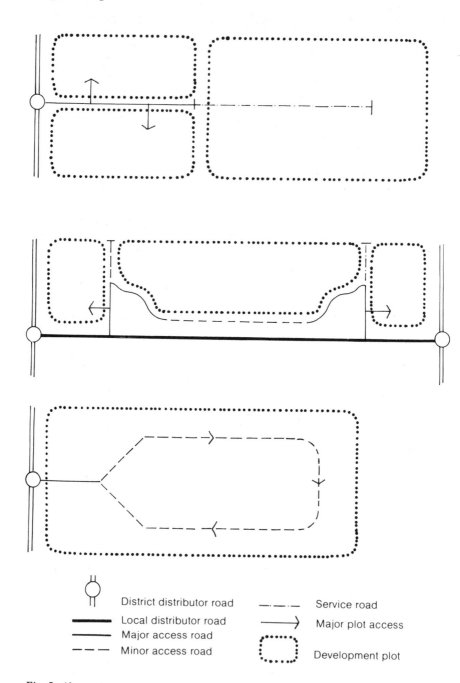

Fig. 5. Alternative arrangements of estate roads

Method of Collection	Storage Requirements
Plastic sacks and refuse compacting vehicles	Sacks in a storage compound near the goods access to each unit [or group of small units]
Wheeled containers and special vehicles	Containers in a storage compound near the goods access with a level, smooth runway to the vehicle
Skips or mini-skips and special vehicles	Concrete skip pads with direct access for the vehicle. Space required for placing empty skip before removal of the full one
Cages for loading on open lorries	Cages are intended for dry waste and have covers to prevent litter blowing away.

Car and lorry parking

The amount of car parking depends partly on the requirements of the local planning authority. These may differ from the developer's assessment of the provision required to satisfy his market. Negotiation may be necessary to resolve differences. The study of traffic generation on industrial estates, referred to previously and described in more detail in Chapter nine, provided aggregated data but suggested that individual estimates should be prepared for each development. These may help to persuade a planning authority that its requirements can be relaxed or met by phased provision of parking spaces.

Car parks should be located as close to the workplace as possible. Whenever possible they should be within the plot curtilage. However for groups of small premises or for buildings occupied by a number of firms a conveniently placed shared car park may be provided.

Basic dimensions for car parking are shown in Fig. 6. As few sites are entirely regular and proper allowance must be made for access and landscaping, it is suggested that for the planning purposes 30sq m per car should be allowed.

Public car parking is only required at estate shopping centres and, possibly, at other estate facilities. A lay-by near the entrance to larger estates is desirable so that visiting drivers can pull in to check directions on arrival.

If an overnight lorry park is needed within the estate, a very high degree of physical security must be provided with an accredited security firm controlling access throughout the day and night. The preferred location will be away from the prime development sites but in a sufficiently prominent position to enhance its security.

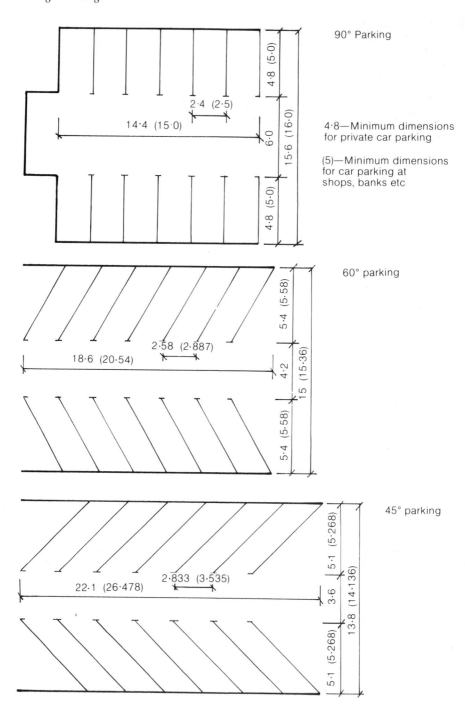

Fig. 6. Alternative arrangements of car parking (all dimensions in metres)

Amenities

Industrial and commercial estates do not easily attract caterers and
shopkeepers because business is confined to a five-day week, with
limited hours of activity, and declines significantly during holiday
periods. To a lesser extent the same considerations apply to banks.
Therefore, the technical team should locate the estate centre to
diversify its trade. There are three possible ways of doing this:-

- Locating the centre on a through route to pick up passing trade
- Establishing the centre at the interface between residential
  and employment areas to attract trade from both
- Establishing an edge-of-town retail centre based on a superstore
  or hypermarket operation with small commercial units adjacent
  [requires detailed negotiation with local planning authority].

Locating an hotel, possibly with conference and leisure facilities, is
unlikely on an industrial estate because of different environmental
requirements and the need for hotels to maximise occupancy at the
weekend as well as during the week. However a well designed business
park might provide a good setting for an hotel particularly if
conferences, exhibitions and recreation are catered for as well.

Provision of public parkland integrated with or adjacent to the site
can also improve an estate's 'commercial' attraction. The location of
land uses and public footpaths must be such as to reduce the risk of
vandalism while minimising the security risks associated with isolated
estates.

Estate management services

The location of premises on the estate to market and manage it must
be considered. Premises could include an estate office and
maintenance depot and, possibly, a security centre. If there is a
concentration of small firms some central office services, including
reception, typing, telex, cleaning and so on, could be provided to
tenants from the estate office. Alternatively a company providing
such services could be attracted to the estate.

Public utilities services

Early planning of the public utilities must be carried out in
conjunction with the statutory undertakers. More information is
contained in Chapter nine but the first essential is to establish
clearly defined reserved routes for all services and site for
associated plant. Routes may also be required for cable televison and
security services.

It is possible that additional piped services such as steam, hot
water, industrial water or compressed air, could be required but the
demand for these is declining and is unlikely to be met by the
developer in present conditions.

Character and environment of the estate

The technical team has to consider the environmental character required by the developer's brief. The requirement can range from attracting high quality employers who will expect an attractive environment and will be prepared to pay a price reflecting the investment necessary to achieve this. At the other end of the scale a local industrial market could cover a wide range of industries and services which would not expect and could not maintain extensive landscaping or sophisticated buildings.

The degree of physical enclosures affects character. A building layout can be very open with low-density landscaping and a minimum of fences and walls. Alternatively it can be designed to enclose views with restricted street pictures and dense landscaping. Each approach is valid in different circumstances. The first may suit an office park while the second may be more appropriate to manufacturing industry with its need to screen untidy activities.

Related to the degree of enclosure is the density of development. Reductions in density involve a twofold penalty on financial performance. They reduce revenue earning floorspace while increasing the residual area requiring maintenance. However, if reduced densities are used to improve the environment and attraction of the estate, increased values may affect this penalty and improve the developer's return.

Building form also determines the character of the estate as does the range of building materials permitted by the developer. Too great a restriction is likely to result in a boring development which potential occupiers will react against. However too great a contrast between buildings may not be acceptable particularly on an enclosed development.

The final critical choice for the planners and the developer together is the selection of those elements on which to concentrate expenditure so as to add the greatest value to the development. For example, a water feature may help to establish the desired image. Alternatively landscaping might be concentrated on a central avenue or a high security environment might be preferred.

Signing

Signing an estate [as distinct from individual premises] has three objectives:

- Marketing   :   Advertising sites and premises
- Identification   :   Announcing the estate and promoting the
                        desired image
- Path finding   :   Guiding visitors around the estate.

Marketing signs are outside the scope of this report, however, identification and pathfinding signs can together contribute to the image of the development. A coherent system of graphics, colours, and a symbol should be used. These may be the house style of the developer or designed for a particular development.

Identification signs at lay-bys near entrances should indicate where enquiries can be made and they may be linked with a map or diagram of the estate layout. Street name plates or direction signs with postal numbers can then be used to guide the visitor to his destination.

The occupants of the estate will have their own corporate identity and the planning team will need to advise the developer on how much freedom of expression should be allowed. It is suggested that detached buildings need few constraints but with parts or units, terraces or blocks, standard locations for signs should be identified with limiting dimensions. Courtyard groups and multi occupancy buildings should be signed at the entrance with single sign displaying all the occupants' names.

Landscape design

This item is covered in detail in Chapter seven. All that is necessary here is to emphasise that landscape is one of the elements of the development plan which needs to be considered as an integral part at all stages as it will mature over the life of the buildings and as a framework for redevelopment when they are replaced.

Areas of tree and shrub planting and grassing should be regarded as a land-use element within the estate. Suitable areas for planting must be reserved on plan and safeguarded against the intrusion of other uses.

Phasing of development

The development of an industrial or commercial estate usually takes 10 to 20 years. There is a need to accept that change during this period is inevitable and the original plan must be robust and adaptable to suit.

The sequence of development should:

- Present a successful aspect as soon as possible
- Establish the main elements of infrastructure so that sites
  can be developed as required
- Avoid premature expenditure
- Keep options open as long as possible.

A first phase is usually situated near the main entrance and an initial advance or pre-let bespoke building erected. This sets the character of the development and early occupation encourages confidence. At the same time main services are brought in and the

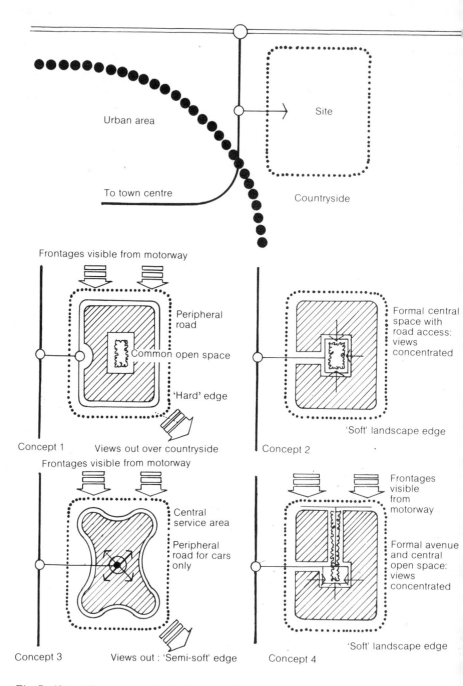

Fig. 7. Alternative concepts: the business park

essential infrastructure is established - if possible with a route through the estate to increase public awareness.

Opportunities for growth need to be identified in the plan. Companies can grow by taking surplus floor space initially; taking vacant adjoining premises; reserving extension land; moving to land held in reserve on the estate by the developer; and lastly by moving away, which is undesirable unless the developer has alternative estates on which it wishes companies to expand.

Whenever possible, extension areas should be grouped so that if extensions are not required, various alternative forms of development are available. This may involve the reservation by the developer of rights of access. The appearance of extension areas can be enhanced by temporary landscaping.

Every large new estate should have a substantial block of land reserved [10%-20% of site area would be a minimum] until the end of the development period so that successful companies can relocate within the estate, minimising removal costs and maintaining their labour force and links with suppliers and customers. It is cheaper to reserve land in this way than in reserved plots within the development.

If existing companies do not grow then the life cycle of the estate can be renewed by bringing in new business. Without expansion space the life cycle of the estate is linked too closely with those of its original tenants who do not renew themselves.

PREPARING AND EVALUATING ALTERNATIVE PLANS

The planning process

The technical team is ready to formulate its proposals when all available information on the site selected for an estate has been collected and the developer's objectives and brief examined and analysed. As it is rarely possible to identify the optimum solution to a planning problem, the team's proposals will aim to satisfy the project objectives to as high a degree as possible within a time-scale acceptable to the developer.

Alternative concepts

A small number of alternative concepts for the project will be identified. These can be expressed in plan form to a small scale. Fig. 7 illustrates the application of this approach to a business park located on the edge of an urban area.

It is unwise to attempt an over-sophisticated evaluation at this stage. Broad estimates of cost can be produced but they should also include an estimate of uncertainty. A range of costs can then be compared with a range of values and the likely upper and lower limits on financial returns established. These will indicate any fundamental problems leading to revision of the brief or even abandonment of the project.

Assuming that this evaluation shows a broadly satisfactory balance the comparison of alternatives can be made by checking each alternative against the functional, aesthetic and financial requirements of the brief. Satisfactory alternatives, which are significantly different in concept, should be selected for further consideration.

Using the example in Fig. 7, concept two might be rejected as not exploiting the motorway frontage. The open space in concept one might be abandoned as having no real function. Concepts three and four may then satisfy the preliminary evaluation.

Alternative plans

More accurate plans of the acceptable concepts are essential at this stage so that the alternatives can be evaluated in terms of certain physical measurements. These will vary according to the type of development proposed but are likely to include the following:

Measurement	Definition	Purpose for which used
LAND USE		
Area of land acquired	Includes any areas acquired but to be excluded from the estate	To identify the developer's acquisition
Gross site area	The area of land for the estate, for example, the total area acquired less any land assigned for other uses, for example, public recreation or residential. Uses ancillary to industry or commerce, for example, flood storage areas, adoptable roads, structural landscaping, estate facilities, and so on, are included	The gross area to which development costs and values must be related The base area for the measurement of developable and ancillary areas

Measurement	Definition	Purpose for which used
Net developable area	Area of land available for development after deduction of ancillary uses. Note: In England, Wales and Northern Ireland the disposal of developable land normally excludes land under adoptable roads on the presumption that it would revert to frontage if the road were stopped up. In Scotland, disposals are normally to the centre line of roads	The area on which development value would be realised if it were sold or leased for building The sum of individual development plots

BUILDING

Floor space – Gross internal area [GIA]	The ground and upper floor areas of buildings measured for lease or sale in accordance with the recommendations of the Royal Institution of Chartered Surveyors	The area on which development value would be realised if the developer built for sale or rent; the sum of speculative floorspace
Floor space – Gross external area [GEA]	As GIA but measured outside the building. This practice is becoming more common in the UK	As for GIA

INFRASTRUCTURE

Road length	The length of adoptable roads [Note: In alternative layouts the costs dependent on a unit of road length are, in broad terms, similar]	To assess the comparative infrastructure efficiency of alternative proposals

Measurement	Definition	Purpose for which used
RATIOS		
Net developable area/ Gross site area	Net developable area as percentage of gross site area	Measures the conversion of land assigned to the estate into developable plots regardless of any decision to build in advance of need.
Floorspace/ Net developable area	GIA or GEA as percentage of net developable area	Measures the density of development on those sites assigned for advance or speculative building where appropriate may be broken down into the different classes of building on the estate
		The density for bespoke building plots depends on the particular user's requirements and cannot be analysed at the planning stage.
Floorspace/ Gross site area	GIA or GEA as percentage of gross site area	This ratio can be used directly if the whole site is to be used for advance or speculative building
Road Length/ Net developable area	Length of adoptable roads per unit of developable area	To compare the efficien of proposals for one estate with that for other estates with similar site conditions and plot sizes

The same measurements should be presented to the developer with estimates of site development costs as they indicate the reasons for particular levels and distributions of elemental costs and will assist the commercial appraisal.

More detailed estimates of site development costs should be prepared when the second stage of evaluation has been completed and detailed improvements made to preferred plans.

Suggested definitions for use in estimating total and unit costs are given below:

Land acquisition cost	The cost of purchasing the freehold of the site including any compensation for tenancies and easements and all the expenses of acquisition
Site preparation cost	The cost of preparing and servicing the site for building excluding all work within the curtilage of developable plots except for regrading and/or ground improvement to these plots; include planning and design fees and expenses; also any off site costs or contributions to local or statutory authorities
Administration cost	An addition should be made to the estimates for the developer's administration costs
Site development cost	The total of land acquisition, site preparation and adminstration costs, for example, the whole cost of bringing a site forward for building construction
Base date	The date on which the prices used in estimates of site development cost are current should be stated. If they are projected, the basis of the forecast is also important
Design and price risk	Estimated costs should include a reasonable percentage addition to cover the probability of increases due to unforeseen items arising during design and to variations in tender price levels
Contingencies	Estimated costs should include a reasonable percentage addition to allow for additional costs arising during construction as a consequence of unforeseen site conditions.

Design risk allows for uncertainties in the design stage and should reduce to nil when design is completed. Allowance for price risk must be made on the basis of anticipated market conditions for a particular project. It would be included in all estimates up to the invitation of tenders. Contingencies are for risks which cannot be foreseen before construction begins.

Unit costs

Ratios

1] $\dfrac{\text{Site development cost}}{\text{Gross Site Area}}$ = £ per ha [acre]

2] $\dfrac{\text{Site development cost}}{\text{Net Developable Area}}$ = £ per ha [acre]

3] $\dfrac{\text{Site development cost}}{\text{Building Area}}$ = £ per sq m [sq ft]

4] Elemental cost as a percentage of total site preparation or development costs

Note: Ratio four needs to be used with caution as one abnormal element will affect the percentages for other elements and therefore reduce the validity of comparisons between proposals.

There are a variety of methods of applying and presenting site development costs on a comparable basis. Appendix two shows a logical form of presentation. This would supplement an analysis of rate of return by showing which elements were at normal cost levels and which were abnormal.

Preferred Plan

The technical team can now produce a preferred plan for presentation to the developer [which should have been involved in its preparation]. The plan should satisfy the developer´s objectives but further planning is necessary before the project can be considered as an investment.

Phasing

Nearly all industrial and commercial estates are developed in phases over a period of years. The way in which this is done has a considerable effect on the marketability of the estate and the financial performance of the developer´s investment.

Various considerations affect phasing: physical constraints such as entry to land and access; commercial criteria such as the market requirements and competitive developments; and such financial considerations as availability of funds [including the generation of funds from the disposal of early phases] and capital grants and tax incentives.

Frequently these considerations will be found to work against each other and it is necessary for the planning team to achieve a balance.

The objectives of the phasing plans and programme should be to achieve the developer´s goal whilst maximising the value of the development at all stages and being adaptable to changes in priorities and in rates of development.

When considering the long-term capital investment required for estate development, the effect of time on the value of money assumes great importance. A discounted cash flow analysis can be employed to establish the present value of the various elements of expenditure and income and to arrive at the net present value of the required investments.

Consultation

The team should ensure during the various stages of planning that the developer is consulted regularly. The developer should also have been advised of importance of adequate consultations with other individuals and authorities and, having given consent, should be advised of the results of all enquiries. Some of the most important are listed below:

- Local planning   Structure and local plans;
  authorities   development control;
                          public rights of way;
                          local facilities; tree
                          preservation orders

- Fire service   Access for fire fighting;
                          water supplies for fire
                          fighting

- Health & Safety   All matters relating to safety
  Executive   during and after development

- Highway authorities   Access; road layouts; standards
  [see Chapter nine]   for highway design/construction;
                          adoption

- Sewerage authorities   Foul and surface water drainage
  [see Chapter eleven]   effluent standards; watercourses;
                          standard for drainage design;
                          adoption

- Public utilities   Existing servicing; water supplies;
  [see Chapter ten]   gas supplies; electricity supplies;
                          telecommunications

– Private services [see Chapter ten]	Existing and proposed services
– Neighbouring landowners	Private rights of way and water rights; tenancies; boundaries; effect of proposed development
– Transport operators	Rail services [passenger/freight]; bus services; taxis/private hire
– Local community	Effect of proposed development.

Consultation with the local community is highly sensitive and if undertaken must be honest and sincere. Any attempt to manipulate the community will lead to future difficulties.

Procedure

The planning process never follows a text book procedure but acceptable proposals are likely to be reached in the shortest time if a programme and list of activities with clearly defined responsibilities for action and reporting are agreed at the outset.

PRESENTATION OF PROPOSALS

The successful presentation of development proposals is an essential step towards their implementation.

"The audience"

A technical team must be prepared to explain its proposals to a wide variety of audiences, each having a different relationship to the project. It must, of course, be prepared for a presentation to the developer which may also require presentations to:

– funding institutions
– planning and statutory authorities
– local community interests

The developer's first concern is that outcome of the proposals should satisfy the objectives of the commercial brief and help it to achieve its business goals. The financial appraisal of the proposed investment will be critical to the developer's decision but it will need sufficient information on technical aspects to give it confidence in the appraisal. The developer may wish to compare the proposals with other developments. It should be made aware of the risks implicit in the proposals – negotiations to be concluded, objections to be overcome and the importance of timing. The technical team's proposals should be made as rationally and impartially as possible and against a background of earlier discussion and understanding.

Funding institutions are primarily interested in the financial appraisal of the proposals; they are unlikely to become closely involved until firm proposals are available. The presentation may concentrate on the choice of location and site, the anticipated market, the objectives of the plan, the quality of the development and the way in which it will be managed and it is likely to be made to a critical audience of professional advisors.

Planning and statutory authorities require sufficient information and explanation to enable them to reach the particular decisions for which they are responsible. A series of separate presentations is recommended. Informal discussions with local planning officers will help to determine whether the formal application needs to be amplified with an explanatory report or presentations to officers and members.

Local community interests should be reflected by the authorities but it is increasingly important to anticipate the reactions of neighbourhood groups and individuals and to explain proposals that will result in changes in the local environment. In general, broad questions of policy are best dealt with through local and statutory authorities while details of design lend themselves to direct discussion with those affected.

Methods of presentation

The choice of presentation method depends on the type of audience and the scale of the proposed development. Information can either be set out for the audience to interpret in its own time [that is, a 'set piece' presentation] or it can be presented face to face so that the presenter can adjust his approach to the reaction of the audience [that is, an 'inter-active' approach]. In practice a combination of methods is often used.

'Set-piece' presentations largely take the form of an illustrated report which has the advantage of economy. It is easily despatched to the intended audience; and provides a permanent reference. Its main disadvantage is that it is difficult for the technical team to know whether the proposals have been understood. For this reason reports are usually used in combination with an inter-active presentation. Reports can be tailored to suit the needs of different audiences. Summaries, conclusions and recommendations should be at the beginning for the busy reader. Financial appraisals should be separately presented for confidential use.

Plans are still the most popular form of graphic presentation but comparatively few people can visualise the physical character of a project from a plan. Perspective drawings can be used to give a better understanding of proposals and an aerial perspective of what is planned in full colour related to an aerial photograph of the site as existing adds an extra dimension to the general view. Perspectives are relatively economical to produce and they are easily transported and reproduced in reports, slides or videotapes.

Scale models are much more costly but are useful tools when it is intended to display development proposals in an exhibition. An exhibition - even a small stand in a local community centre or shop - is a useful means of reaching those affected by the proposals. The same display can be used as an aid to presentation in official or public meetings.

The technical team members need to learn the skills required for the presentation of proposals at meetings.

Three simple guidelines:

- Few audiences remain receptive for more than 20 minutes; if conditions are uncomfortable this time is reduced

- Non-specialist audiences take in only a small number of facts at one sitting; the presentation must concentrate on the most important

- For non-technical audiences it is usually best to select one member of the team to make the presentation; two or more speakers take longer and increase the risk of repetition.

Where the same presentation is scheduled for a number of occasions, an audio-visual presentation may be recorded on audio tape and photographic slides or on video tape. The first is more suited to large public meetings and committees; the second is ideal as an introduction to a discussion with small groups.

´Inter-active´ presentations involve at least invitation to comment on a report or the answering of questions raised in a face to face meeting. Beyond these lies debate or negotiation.

Although it is best for one member of a team to make a presentation, all the principal professions need to be represented in debate, with one member leading the discussion [unless the developer takes this role]. The objective should be to reach a sound understanding of the comments made by the audience; to answer questions and comments constructively; to overcome objections where possible; and to note items for future consideration when they cannot be dealt with in the meeting. The team should never aim to score debating points.

Where the discussion follows the issue of a report or an audio-visual presentation it is important that display material should be available and referred to by the team; at the end of a meeting any ´follow-up´ action should be agreed.

The use of press, radio and television will depend on the objectives of the developer. It is likely to take specialist advice in public relations if it makes use of these media and the planning team's role may be restricted to providing information and preparing illustrations suitable for publication.

In conclusion, it must be pointed out that any approach which relies on concealing information or on manipulating the audience is likely to be against the developer's interest in the long run.

APPROVALS AND AGREEMENTS

At the conclusion of the planning stage for any project the team will need to obtain a series of approvals before the project can proceed. These can be summarised under the following headings:

- Developer's
- Funding
- Planning
- Highways
- Sewerage
- Building Regulations
- Environmental health
- Health and safety at work
- Advertisements and signs
- Private agreements.

Developer's and funding approvals

These are the first priority for the team and must be related to each stage set out in the brief from the developer. The team should tell the developer what commitments are essential initially and what commitments need be in principle only.

Funding institutions will require certain technical approvals which the team should obtain so that the developer's negotiations can proceed smoothly.

Planning Permission

The majority of estate developments require permission for development under General Development orders made under the Town & Country Planning Acts except for those regulated by Special Development Order applying to areas such as new towns or enterprise zones. The latter are subject to particular procedures which are not dealt with here.

If the team believes the proposed land uses conform with an existing use or permission it can apply for a Certificate of Established Use or a Certificate of Alternative Use. These will relate to land use only and permission will still be required for the details of development.

Outline permission can be obtained at an early stage if there is to be a change of use. This is not essential as full planning permission can be obtained irrespective of whether an outline permission has been granted. Development must be begun within five years of the granting of planning permission.

Planning application forms require details of the proposed development and must be accompanied by location, site and development plans. Certificates regarding ownership of the land or confirming notification of the owners in a prescribed form must accompany applications. Fees are payable to local planning authorities on submission of applications.

Land uses are classified in use class orders issued under the Town & Country Planning Acts. Current trends in industrial and commercial development have tended to make classification more difficult but it is still important to funding institutions that the permitted uses should be clearly defined by the planning permission, generally with specific reference to the dominant use-class permitted. The government has discouraged planning authorities from attempting to restrict ancillary uses [for instance, offices in a manufacturing plant] unless there is a material change of use.

Applications for industrial, offices, warehousing, storage and retail uses require additional details relating to floorspace, employment, business traffic and hazardous materials.

Planning application forms appear to have been drafted with individual buildings in mind rather than estate development. As a result considerable care is required to ensure that permission is obtained for:

- The proposed land-use over the whole area
- The particular site preparation and building works
  that the developer requires

Applications may be accompanied by supporting material which does not in itself form part of the application. The report of the technical team could assist the authority in reaching a decision.

Planning authorities are required to consider applications within eight weeks and to advise the applicant if they cannot be decided in this time. However they are not cleared automatically after this date and the applicant is usually offered a choice of extension of time or rejection.

The local planning authority may impose conditions as part of its approval. These conditions must be confined to matters on which the authority is empowered by the Planning Acts, and the planning team should examine the granting of permission with great care and advise the developer of any conditions that are 'ultra-vires'. If a planning application is refused or unacceptable conditions are imposed the technical team should advise the developer on the timing and content of an appeal to the appropriate Secretary of State.

The local planning authority can only impose conditions which can be discharged on land controlled by the applicant. If a condition that it wishes to impose cannot be discharged because the applicant does not control the land affected, the authority would have to reject the application. To overcome this difficulty the authority can enter into a separate legal agreement with the applicant and planning permission will not be granted until this has been completed.

Highways

It is important that agreement is reached with the highway authority at an early date in order to agree details of roads to be maintained at public expense. When these details have been agreed a legal agreement is entered into in order that the roads may formally be adopted after completion and 12 months' satisfactory maintenance. Private roads to be maintained by the developer are dealt with under the Building Regulations.

Sewerage

Similar procedures are required by sewerage authorities for the design, construction and, if required, adoption of foul and surface water sewers.

Consent will also be required for the discharge of surface water or treated effluent into water courses.

Building Regulations approval

Most construction works for estate development are required to comply with the Building Regulations under which plans must be deposited with the local authority and the prescribed notice given for each stage of the works. Unlike planning permission, approval under the Building Regulations is not a mandatory requirement for work to begin. It is prudent to obtain approval in advance as the regulations are open to interpretation and subsequent argument and abortive works can be avoided.

Environmental health

The local authority's environmental health officer should be consulted about all matters under his control. These include pollution of the environment from noise and air-borne fumes and dust; working conditions in offices; shops and railway premises; and establishments dealing with food. Some of these controls will be exercised through conditions in the planning permission. Others will require specific approval.

Health and safety at work

Matters affecting the health and safety of those affected by the development - either during or after construction - are the responsibility of the Health & Safety Executive. Some of its requirements will be incorporated in planning conditions [for example, those relating to the storage of hazardous materials]. Others will require separate approval.

The executive generally operates through the issue of notices in respect of any hazard that is reported to it or identified by its officials. It can require the removal of a hazard or, where necessary, it can stop work on a site. It is prudent for the planning team to consult the executive as early as possible if a hazard is suspected.

Advertisements and signs

The display of advertisements is controlled by advertisement regulations which are administered by the local planning authority. Signs within certain dimensions are permitted; others require specific approval which is granted for a specific period and can be renewed.

Private agreements

Discussions with adjoining owners during the planning stages may result in formal agreement [for instance, for the termination or diversion of a private right, or for the adjustment of a boundary]. Following the approval of its proposals the technical team should provide the developer's solicitors with all the information necessary for completion of a legal agreement.

When all the necessary approvals and formal agreements have been obtained or programmed the project moves forward to the implementation stage for advance site preparation works.

MONITORING AND REVIEW

As already mentioned, the development plan for an estate will require revision during the development period. The advantage of careful planning could be lost if changes are made without proper consideration. The developer may retain the services of the technical team to ensure the controlled flexibility that he desires.

Monitoring

Control will require the monitoring of information on progress, land use, employment, utility services and financial performance.

Review

The team will compare this data with the plan at agreed intervals and identify significant variations. It will consider short-comings in the plan and programme; examine charges in competitive and complementary developments; and propose revisions for the developer's approval.

REFERENCES AND FURTHER READING

JAMIESON MACKAY AND PARTNERS: Scottish Development Agency. Industrial and commercial estate traffic generation. Part 1: Surveys and analysis; Part 2: Procedures for estimating traffic generation. Reports prepared for Joint Technical Committee. Thomas Telford Limited, London, 1985.

Acts of Parliament and Statutory Instruments. (In most cases, different Acts and Statutory Instruments apply in England, Wales, Scotland and Northern Ireland.) All published by HMSO, London.

Government circulars. Relevant circulars are issued for: England and Wales - Jointly by the Department of the Environment (DoE) and the Welsh Office; Scotland - by the Scottish Office; Northern Ireland - by the DoE (Northern Ireland). All published by HMSO.

Chapter 7

LANDSCAPING

INTRODUCTION

Requirements for landscaping vary considerably from site to site but should be carefully considered at the earliest stage in the development process. The type of landscaping and maintenance requirement best suited to the project should be determined, thereby avoiding last minute 'cosmetic' work to tidy up unsightly corners.

It is necessary clearly to identify "structure" landscaping that can be implemented at an early stage in conjunction with the initial site development works. Structure landscaping as opposed to the landscaping works related to building sets the tone of the project and provides a framework for future design.

Landscape design involves the following elements:

- Survey

Site boundaries; topography; slope; orientation and aspect; local climate; subsoil - quality, quantity, toxicity; topsoil - quality, quantity, toxicity; vegetation - existing, local; services; other factors, for example, flood plain

- Analysis

Site factors: locality; unbuildable ground; site resources and opportunities; visual analysis

Off site factors: type of development; development density; budget; time-scale; planning requirements

- Design

Structure landscaping; hard landscaping; detailed landscaping around buildings; design for maintenance

- Maintenance

Principles; responsibility; operation

SURVEYS

Mistakes occur on site as a result of inaccurate or insufficient information. It is important to establish those factors which are most likely to affect development and to specify at the outset the survey information to be collected and the way it is to be presented. This presentation would normally take the form of a "constraints" plan and sufficient time must be allowed to establish a proper data base. The approach to data gathering must be methodical though it will be to a degree determined by each project.

All surveys must include site limitations; good level information; a vegetation and tree survey; a soil survey; plus location of services and restrictions on planting.

Site boundaries

A clear definition of the limitations of the site area should be given together with relevant information about areas outside the site boundaries so that the estate layout and landscaping are set in their proper context.

Topography

The site should be surveyed to scales which are normally 1:500 and 1:200. Contours should be plotted at one metre intervals. When extensive earthworks are likely these should be defined at the survey stage to ensure early input from the landscape architect.

Slope

A slope analysis should be carried out in developments of over 10 ha. Selection of slopes will be determined by the project but, as a general rule, five grades can be identified:

- Very steep ... 1:3 - 1:10
- Steep .... 1:10 - 1:20
- Moderate ..... 1:20 - 1:60
- Gentle .... 1:60 - 1:100
- Very gentle .. over   1:100

Orientation and aspect

The primary orientation of the site should be noted together with significant points of aspects both looking into the site and looking from the site.

North facing slopes should be avoided for public areas and for

80

principal entrance to buildings if a more decorative landscape treatment, requiring adequate sunlight, is deemed necessary.

Local climate

Local climate has an effect not only on the rate of plant growth but on the growth of plant types.

Usually the following problems can be identified from site visits, observation of plant growth and conversation with local people:

- Sheltered areas
- Frost pockets
- Wind funnels
- Areas of excessive rainfall
- Altitude
- Damp hollows
- Coastal areas where salt spray occurs.

It is important to establish the ground water level particularly close to mature trees. Problems can arise from altering this level as a result of development of building works.

Subsoil

The condition of the subsoil is extremely important and can strongly influence the choice of plant materials, tree species and so on, as well as the overall design of land form.

Subsoil quality is particularly crucial on land reclamation schemes, especially if toxic wastes such as heavy metals are present. If evidence of waste is found, experience has shown that it is essential to locate the material and determine what should be done about it.

The subsoil should be tested for toxicity and pH value in order to ensure there is no risk to successful plant establishment. It might be possible if the site is devoid of topsoil that the subsoils can, with suitable treatment, be grassed and planted.

Topsoil

Topsoil is defined by BS 388 : 1965 and refers to the top 150mm–130mm fertile layer of earth which will generally be high in humus and fibre and capable of supporting living plants. The availability and cost of topsoil can be one of the most significant factors in the achievement of good landscaping. Misuse of existing topsoil can result in the need to import expensive replacement material. The quality and quantity available should be identified and tests should be made for pH value, structure and organic content.

In England and Wales, the Soil Survey of England and Wales, and in Scotland, the Macauley Institute for Research, Craigiebuckler Aberdeen, provide soil survey maps. However, they tend not to be of sufficient detail for individual site development work and site samples need to be taken for analysis.

Engineering borehole information is not a reliable measure for the depth of topsoil which should be ascertained independently by the landscape architect. In addition to its depth, the topsoil's pH value and nutrient levels should be established by simple laboratory tests.

Topsoil when being reused should be free from stones larger than 50 mm, perennial weeds and rotting plant and other extraneous material. If no topsoil is present, an assessment of topsoil requirement should be made, based on the following guide depths:

- Grass   -   100/150mm minimum
- Shrubs/feathered trees   -   300mm
- Trees   -   1cu m/tree pit

All finished topsoil levels should finish 25mm above kerb levels, manholes or other hard surfaces. Topsoil should be stored in low mounds 2m high. Greater than this will cause a loss of soil structure. If the soil is not to be respread within one year, then the heap should be turned over to avoid it becoming sour.

Vegetation

Accurate plotting of existing trees, hedgerows and shrubs is essential. The value in retaining existing vegetation is now recognised [there are Acts of Parliament to ensure retention in certain circumstances] and a careful survey of the type and condition of existing vegetation must be made if it is to be retained. A note should also be made of vegetation on adjacent land as this can help to determine the character of the new site planting.

Services

Information on existing and proposed services should be obtained and assembled on one drawing in order to assess their impact on the landscape design. Services can impose a restriction on the landscape design but it must be recognised that servicing the site must have priority. Public utilities do impose restrictions on the proximity of planting and these should be checked out with the appropriate board in order that it can be considered at the design stage.

Generally, tree planting is not allowed between 3m - 5m from a pipe or cable. The zone of restriction may be greater if high voltage cables, major gas and water mains are involved. But there is less reason why shrub planting should not take place over service lines and most authorities allow this except where major lines exist.

There are restrictions above ground too, such as clearances required to accommodate the swing of overhead cables.

Other factors

Every site has its own characteristics and very often its own unique features. Such features can be natural or man-made and should be incorporated in the estate design. Such a feature identifies the site and can help in terms of identity and marketing.

A visual survey by the landscape architect provides a general 'feel' for the site in its area. In addition, it also allows for the opportunity to identify materials such as stone and so on, for reuse which otherwise might have been removed from site.

ANALYSIS

The division between survey and analysis is often blurred. However the main points regarding analysis can be listed as follows:

- Site factors
- Off site factors
- Budget
- Time-scale of effect
- Time-scale of implementation
- Planning requirements

Site factors

The locality of the site is often ignored and standard designs of spaces and details are applied which can lead to all sites adopting a predominantly suburban character. The information obtained in the survey should provide for a more sensitive approach allowing the proposed landscaping to be more sympathetic to the site's surroundings.

Unbuildable land such as steep slopes, areas of poor ground bearing capacity and so on, should be regarded as an opportunity to form the basis of an open space pattern for the estate.

Site resources [that is, existing material which can be reused] have an asset value which needs careful assessment. In general, reuse is a very attractive proposition but extremely careful planning and record keeping is essential, otherwise any gain will rapidly turn out more expensive and time consuming. All arrangements for removal and temporary storage, for example, should be kept simple.

Visual analysis is often one of the most useful, quick and yet most infrequently carried out analyses. A diagrammatic plan is useful which either by tones or symbols clearly defines the visual qualities of the site both from within and outside the site. Buildings of particular value, focal points or other important features should all be included.

Off site factors

The type of development must come from the developer´s brief and should be clearly stated and the landscape solution must echo the developer´s requirement of the image and environment he wishes to create. It is important the right level of expenditure be allowed in order to achieve this image.

In general, industrial estates achieve a development density of ground floor area to site of between 30% and 40%. Between 60% and 70% of the site therefore is not built upon and consists of roadway, yards, parking and open space. It is not the quantity of open space that is paramount for a good design but its location and quality within the estate. Low density does not necessarily lead to good landscaping.

Other factors that can affect the site density and landscape proposals are junction spacing, sight lines, turning areas, building lines and expansion areas and all must be carefully considered.

It is important that the proposed density of development is known at the analysis stage. Density may be described as follows:

Class	Percentage of developable plot area
High density	Over 40% building coverage
Medium density	30% – 40% building coverage
Low density	Under 30% building coverage

Budget

The money allocated in the development budget to the landscaping of an estate must be clearly defined in terms of how much, when and what will be available for maintenance. This money must be seen as part of the overall investment to create the right type of estate for its purpose; to provide an attractive environment for prospective tenants and not to create a long-term financial burden by way of excessive maintenance requirements.

The time-scale of development, effect required and budgets should all be identified for the landscape designer.

In general the earlier a landscape scheme is implemented, the more cost-effective it will be. Advanced planting can be highly desirable bearing in mind that care must be taken not to plant up areas which could be required for building within five years' time. The expansion areas related to individual buildings can be economically treated in order to avoid very open and uninteresting landscape. The designer can allow for successful modification at moderate cost throughout the development of an estate which may take many years using such techniques as sacrificial shelter belt planting.

Time-scale of effect

It is important to assess how quickly a landscape design will impact on the site and how much any existing features will help that impact. In considering the time-scale of effect, it is essential to establish critical thresholds, particularly the height of planting. It is proposed that for industrial areas there are four critical heights:

- 1m   :   below eye level   : buildings dominate
- 1.8m :   just above eye level   : planting has first major
                                       impact/screening
- 6m   :   planting begins to appear
           above units   : buildings obscured
- 20m :   planting dominant   : maturity

[The average growth rate of trees in the UK is between 300mm-500mm a year].

The choice of species is also important and a two or three stage long-term effect can be achieved by mixing fast growing varieties with slower growing types, as shown in Fig. 8. A continuing effect will be achieved if the faster growing species are thinned out or removed once the slower growing varieties reach maturity.

Time-scale of implementation

It should be noted that the implementation of landscape works is seasonal and there are many regional variations. The following give some indication of time-scale:

- Grass sowing   :   April-May to September-October
- Shrub and tree planting   :   November to March
- Bulb planting   :   October
- Turf laying   :   February to November

These approximate times can be greatly affected by weather conditions and delays of up to a year may be encountered.

Planning requirements

Planning requirements such as tree preservation orders will have been picked up in the survey. However, at the analysis stage, discussions should take place with local planning officials to determine the planning department's attitude to landscaping, what its requirements might be and how and when this information is to be submitted. Structure plans affecting the area should be consulted as this will often set the authority's requirements in context.

In most cases, the above information and appraisal of the assets and liabilities of the site will allow a draft zoning plan to be prepared showing the broad pattern of built form, access and landscape. From the analysis, development guidelines or a brief can be prepared and a site plan agreed.

DESIGN

Industrial and commercial estates have of necessity to accommodate buildings of varied size, shape and appearance. The numerous activities related to these buildings can result in visual and physical clutter. Landscaping provides the opportunity to counter these less desirable effects with designs and planting that are strong, resilient and simple without becoming monotonous.

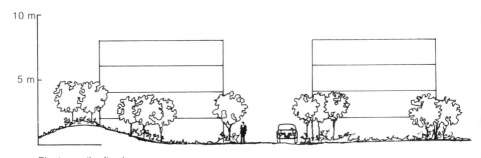

Plant growth after 1 year
— buildings and landform dominate

During the interim period, shrubs provide
an effective screen at eye-level

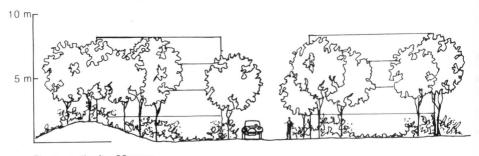

Plant growth after 20 years
— trees begin to contain buildings and space

Fig. 8. Landscaping time-scale

At all stages, good industrial landscape design should be structured to contain development; present variety and interest; be capable of being well maintained and kept tidy; help to attract investment; be able to flourish and grow; and because of the unique scale of industrial development, have a well-defined tree coverage.

The main phases of landscape design are:

Structure landscaping

Structure landscaping provides an order and backcloth for the development but requires space which must be present from the start. It can assist in building up the spatial organisation and hierarchy of a site, which can be split into a number of components:

- Entrances which will reflect the quality of the site
- Main routes which can involve avenue planting and/or broad open space
- Front/back spaces next to buildings which often involve hard areas
- Pedestrian routes which may be separated from roads
- Controlled vistas which can be created both internally and externally.

The techniques to achieve structure landscaping can include main blocks of forestry planting, avenue planting, sacrificial site planting, landform such as open rolling topography illustrated in Fig. 9, boundary planting and linear open space routes developed on existing features such as a river.

Detail landscaping around buildings

Detail landscape design will form a substructure to the main landscape structure and demands a great deal of care and attention. It is associated with the need to screen yards and car parks, ensure adequate road sight lines and immediate recreation facilities for the occupiers of the buildings. Fig. 10 illustrates good landscape practice in screening yard areas. Industrial estates are occupied all year and the deciduous nature of much planting makes it most important to introduce species to provide winter colour; for example, evergreen and coloured stemmed deciduous species.

Hard landscaping

The primary use and function of hard landscape in industrial areas is to carry vehicle and pedestrian traffic. Secondary functions are to separate uses, take up level changes and to provide an alternative ground cover. Functional considerations are often the only method by which materials are chosen. At present the image of hard landscape in industrial areas is that of large expanses of tarmac or concrete in

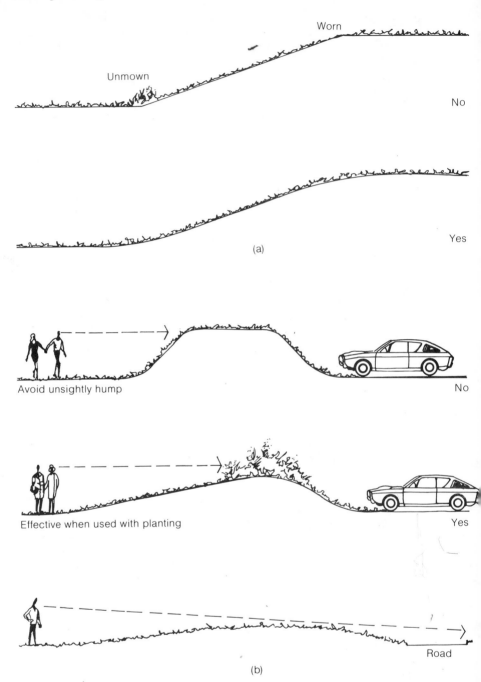

Fig. 9. Land form: (a) shape of slope; (b) mounding to screen cars (upper) and to reduce areas of tarmac (lower)

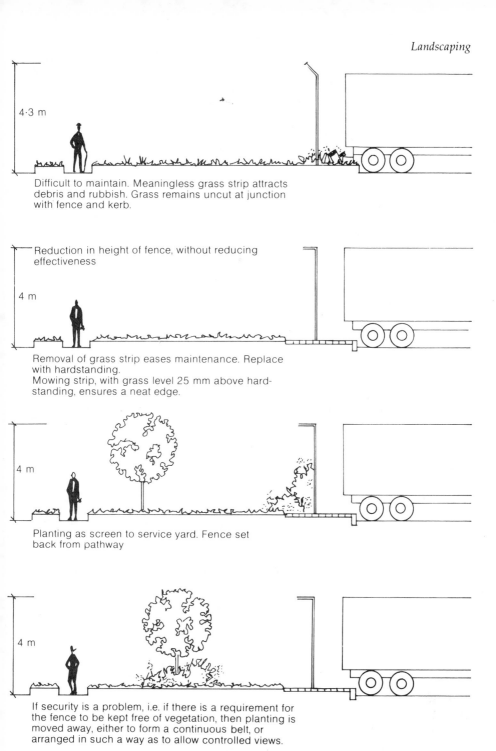

Difficult to maintain. Meaningless grass strip attracts debris and rubbish. Grass remains uncut at junction with fence and kerb.

4·3 m

Reduction in height of fence, without reducing effectiveness

4 m

Removal of grass strip eases maintenance. Replace with hardstanding.
Mowing strip, with grass level 25 mm above hardstanding, ensures a neat edge.

4 m

Planting as screen to service yard. Fence set back from pathway

4 m

If security is a problem, i.e. if there is a requirement for the fence to be kept free of vegetation, then planting is moved away, either to form a continuous belt, or arranged in such a way as to allow controlled views.

Fig. 10. Service yard surrounds

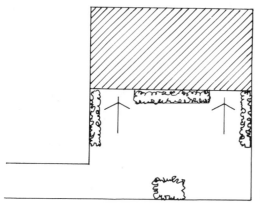

Often many small spaces are created. Planting is prone to damage, makes little impact and is expensive to implement and maintain.

No — too fussy

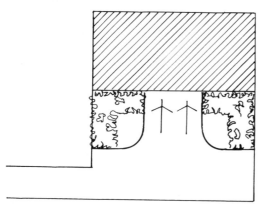

Yes — Spaces are brought together and planting can be in scale with the building.

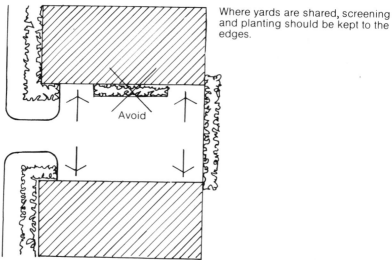

Where yards are shared, screening and planting should be kept to the edges.

Avoid

Fig. 11. Service yard layouts

service yards, wide roads and parking areas with little or no delineation between various activities.

The actual building design can help to reduce the impact of hard surfaces. Grouping of access doors will concentrate service yard space, and the position of main entrances can ensure smooth transition from car park and footpaths to the front door. The grouping of access doors illustrated in Fig. 11 allows for a more effective combination of soft and hard landscaping.

Varying functions of hard surfaces adjacent to units [that is, car parks and service access] can be clearly defined by changes in material. By this method confusion can be minimised, efficiency improved and large open paths established.

While the correct use of well chosen materials will generally result in a reduction of hard landscape, there will be occasions when hard landscape will be more appropriate than soft. Good use can be made of hard materials around buildings and service yards, as edges, trims and borders. Gravel, or blockwork is a good alternative to planting in the often 'left-over' space between building and footpath.

Careful consideration should be given to using the most appropriate material in terms of cost, appearance and even tradition. Colour, texture, detailing and junctions must all be considered.

Block paving is a possible alternative to tarmac or concrete, either wholly or in part. Not only does it tend to look more attractive, but function can be easily defined by changes of colour. Arguably, block paving is more resilient than other materials in large areas, is certainly easier to replace and maintain, and provides easy access to underground servicing.

Materials available include:

- Tarmac/bitmac/asphalt: variety of textured finishes; best used for access roads and footpaths

- Concrete: versatile, with paviors, setts, slabs and in situ in almost any colour or texture. Roads, paths, trims and service yards

- Brick: most appropriate in areas of established brick tradition. For lightly trafficked footpaths as well as walls and trims

- Stone: attractive but very expensive - but can continue tradition

- Clay paviors: similar use to brick but generally harder wearing; good for vehicle parking

- Cobbles: used as trim but often incorrectly as deterrent
          paving

- Granite/whin setts: expensive, often available secondhand;
          extremely hard wearing

- Gravel: used as trim or footpaths. Should be kept 25 mm
          below kerb line to avoid spillage

- Boulders: can be used as features if available

- Timber: rarely used, except for fencing. Slippery when wet

Other elements can be introduced, not only to add interest as
permanent features in industrial estates, but also to assist the
creation of space, screening and delineation, before planting has
reached maturity. Ideally, industrial estates should have a corporate
identity, with all artefacts and materials forming an association with
the buildings, and with each other.

Lighting, bollards, walls, fences and gates, drainage channels and
gullies, steps and handrails - all can help create an identity for an
estate and thereby assist marketing to prospective tenants and
purchasers.

Design for maintenance

The landscape of any industrial area is never static: its appearance
is a function of two equal factors, the original design and its
subsequent maintenance. Set out below are several ways in which
correct preparation linked to design can help maintenance.

- Ground preparation
- Grass areas
- Shrub planting
- Tree planting.

Good ground preparation is essential to ensure good growth which is
itself an aid to good maintenance. On completion of the building works
and prior to the spreading of topsoil, the ground should be
decompacted, particularly in areas where plant or temporary buildings
have been standing. Areas of diesel spillage or cement/lime deposits
should be dug out and removed from site as should all bricks and
rubbish.

Correct topsoil depths have already been referred to but it is worth
repeating that finished topsoil levels must be 25mm above kerbs to
allow for settlement.

Ground shape and slope have a significant effect on maintenance.
Practice has shown that, if close mown grass is required using a
power mower, slopes should be restricted to a maximum of 1:3. All

slopes, unless designed to create exaggerated landform, should be rounded off at both the top and bottom to avoid the growth of long grass at the foot and scalping at the top as shown in Fig. 9.

It is usually better to treat steep slopes by species either forestry planting or ground cover shrubs. In many instances where space is restricted, a low retention structure can help to reduce the slope and provide a neat, manageable edge at the foot of the banking.

It is possible for the designer to identify high and low priority grass areas to help organise maintenance programmes. Levels of turf in relation to surroundings should be carefully considered to ease mowing.

Shrub beds greater than 3m wide can be difficult to maintain economically, although, if ground cover plants are used, can be extremely attractive. Equally small narrow beds can be difficult to establish and maintain. These areas are prone to abuse by people walking over them or storing pallets on them and in many circumstances should be treated with a suitable hard surface.

The choice of plant material which will grow and cover the ground well is important if extensive and continual weeding is to be avoided. A balance must be struck between fast growing shrubs which may be short-lived and slow-growing species which require four years plus to establish.

Correct plant spacing will help cover to be established quickly with initial impact and at optimum cost. Recommended distances are given in Table 3 below.

Table 3. Plant Spacing

Initial plant height	Established habit	Cover with examples
1 600mm – 900mm	tall-medium shrubs	3/sq m elder willow rosa viburnum
2 400mm – 500mm	lower-growing shrubs	5/sq m potentilla lonicera spiraea
3 300mm spread	ground cover	7 – 9/sq m hypericum pachysandra vinca

Mixed shrub beds do not require extensive pruning as for example, rose beds. The technique of layer planting, with lower compact shrubs to the front, will again reduce pruning.

Trees may be classified into groups: those planted to form structure or woodland and those planted individually either in avenue or general group form. With structure planting, maintenance will be aided if the trees are planted on a grid of either 1.5m or 2m centres. Although this may create an artificial appearance initially, it does allow men clearly to locate young planting either for weak spraying or using mechanical aids to cut the vegetation.

The edge details of structure planting should be carefully considered. Traditionally, post and wire fencing is used. Straining post must be regularly checked for firmness. Styles rather than gates should be provided for maintenance access as they are less prone to damage or wear and tear.

Where structure planting meets a road or footpath, a mown grass verge of at least 1.2m width should be provided to form a neat edge. A further aid to edging structure planting is to plant a hedge, whose maintenance is reduced by modern power take off hedge trimmers. Maintenance is increased with trees grouped together or used individually in grass. It is important that care is taken in their location. All too often "circles" are arbitrarily drawn on plans with little thought of impact and maintenance.

When used as avenue planting, trees should be a minimum of 4m apart for ease of mowing and set at least 1.2m back from the footpath or road. There should be an area of 400mm diameter around the base of each tree which is to be kept clear of grass weeds. Initially, this may be by hand hoeing, later by weedkiller. Alternatively, a tree mat can be used.

Trees should be well staked and tied with, if possible, the stakes facing the line of mowing to reduce the chance of impact damage by mowers. The grouping of trees in longer grass not only enables gang mowers to cut the open grass areas more efficiently, but reduces the number of grass cuts in the tree planted area.

MAINTENANCE

A landscape management procedure or plan is essential to maintain the open spaces to a required standard at an acceptable cost.

Aftercare maintenance on completion of the contract is a most crucial period for landscape work. It is normally a 12 month period following practical completion during which the contractor is responsible for the regular upkeep, maintenance and establishment of the landscape works. These operations must be adequately described and priced at the time of tendering. A period of at least three years for establishment maintenance follows the aftercare period and can be let as a separate contract either annually or for the full length of the establishment period.

The ongoing maintenance has to be considered in terms of responsibility. It must be clearly laid down whether the developer or his tenants will be responsible for this work.

Maintenance operations are seasonally related and their timing is defined in Table 4. The Table indicates the minimum operations. The summer months, in particular the early summer, provide the greatest strain on maintenance. The techniques associated with the maintenance operations are wide-ranging and require experienced advice. They are summarised in the following pages.

Table 4. Landscape maintenance chart of operations

Operation	Jan	Feb	Mar	Apr	May	June	July	Aug	Sept	Oct	Nov	Dec
1 Grass												
Cutting			- -	━	━	━	━	━	━	━	- -	
Fertilizer application			━	━	━	━	━	━	━			
Herbicide application				━	━			━	━			
Aeration	━	━	- -	- -				- -	- -	━		
Grazing												
2 Trees												
Grass/weed control			- -	━	━	━	━	━	━	━	- -	
Fertislier			━									
Firming	━	━	- -									━
Pruning	━	━	━							━	━	━
Replanting	━	━	━								━	━
Insecticide application					- -	━	━	- -				
3 Shrubs												
Weed control			- -	━	━	━	━	━	━	━	- -	
Fertiliser			━							━		
Firming	━	━	━							━		
Pruning	━	━	━	━						━		
Replanting	━	━	━	- -	- -	- -				━		
Mulching		━	━							━		
Insecticide					- -	━	━	- -				
4 Other												
Litter collection	━	━	━	━	━	━	━	━	━	━	━	━
Snow clearance	━	━	━								━	━

95

Grass

The normal maintenance operations are:
- cutting : maintaining the correct height of grass will determine the appearance and to some extent resistance to wear of the grass. Table 5 below shows the frequency per annum and height of cuts.

Table 5. Grass Cutting

Priority area	Frequency	Height
HIGH - high amenity entrances, approaches, "front doors"	14-20	25mm-35mm
MEDIUM - general areas, expansion areas, general open space	6-10	35mm-50mm
LOW - remote areas or planted banking. Rural	2-6	100mm

- Aeration: For good turf this is an essential and inexpensive operation. Forking, spiking or slitting are best done in the spring and autumn. Good quality grass areas should have their cuttings removed and be raked to remove dead grass and moss in the autumn.

- Fertiliser: All grass areas benefit from an annual dressing of fertiliser, in particular nitrogen. Many manufacturers produce slow release granular fertilisers which work throughout the summer.

- Herbicide: Regular mowing will generally eradicate most perennial weeds, but it may be necessary on high amenity lawn areas to use a selective herbicide to remove broad-leaved weeds. This is best done in May and late August/early September but not in periods of drought.

Trees

The need for and type of tree maintenance depends upon the age of a tree and whether it is planted singularly or in a plantation. In general, the need in young trees is to reduce the competition from weeds while in elder trees it is the removal of dead or dying branches and stability checks which are important.

- Individually planted young trees
Trees in industrial areas are usually planted as selected standards, heavy and extra heavy standards, and they are staked and tied. In

the first few years, stakes and ties must be regularly checked.
After five years, they may be removed. Little pruning is usually
necessary. Suckers [especially common in poplars, lime] should be
removed from the base and dead branches and twigs removed. Lack of
growth is often an indication of poor tree pit preparation. Steps
should be taken to replant trees correctly during the winter.

- Young trees in plantations
The competition from weeds should be reduced as with single trees.
Two techniques can be applied:

> Complete bare earth; chemical control using
> paraquat/simazine

> Weed growth control only at base of plants,
> with spot application of chemicals, hand hoe

Warning - Both techniques require management and operative skill.
When chemicals are used, there should be no drift and checks should be
made with manufacturers that the tree species are not susceptible to
prolonged exposure to the chemical. Proper arbor guards must be fitted
when using strimmers otherwise bark will be stripped. Timing is also
vital, particularly getting a good start in March.

Regular checks should be made for disease especially during mild
weather.

In addition, checks should be made for firmness after gales and in
very dry weather, especially in the first three years. The "whipping"
effect of some plants can be reduced by cutting hard back after
planting, with poplar, willow, elder species for example.

Older trees

After 10 to 15 years, woodlands are ready for first thinning; next,
in 25 years; final, in 50 years. After the first five years, it is
generally not necessary to fertilise except on reclaimed sites.
Check for and make good drainage if it develops.

- Older trees: individual
Very little maintenance is required for older trees. Check for
health and if branches appear dead or top heavy, remove by using a
qualified tree surgeon.
The need to fell any tree will depend upon age and individual site
conditions and problems rather than blanket rules.

- Older trees in plantation
Very little maintenance is required for these either, but the
plantation should never be taken for granted. The aim should be to
achieve a good age spread, therefore selective felling and planting
are good practice.

A watch should be kept for disease and in dry weather for potential fire hazards.

Shrubs

Weed and litter control provide the two common difficult and expensive maintenance items for shrub planted area, particularly during the aftercare and establishment period. In mass shrub planting, the aim is to establish a complete cover to the ground as soon as practicable. The amount of light reaching the soil is reduced with this cover and weed growth suppressed. There are principally three methods of weed control:

- Hand hoe
- Chemical
- Mulching.

The advantage of hand hoeing over chemical control is the soil structure is improved and the danger of accidental spray damage to susceptible young shoots and plants is reduced. Herbicides, especially residual, should only be used on established areas unless great care is taken. As the shrub beds mature, they will require less hand cultivation, but it is good practice to fork over the beds prior to winter and in the spring.

Chemical weed control has now become an important part of soft landscape maintenance. Many areas of planting may be kept free of weed growth for 12 months, thereby greatly reducing the labour cost.

Herbicides may be classified as contact [that is, they kill only plant they come in contact with] or residual [that is, remain in soil, stop growth]. In addition, they may be selective in that they kill only specific weeds, or nonselective, killing all plants.

Herbicides must be used with care and applied by fully trained staff, and at the right time. They are particularly useful in two circumstances:

- Eradication of persistant perennial weeds, for example, Glyphosate
- Complete weed control on established beds, for example, Simazine

Peat, bark and general compost are all used for mulching. The aim of a mulch is to cover the surface usually to a depth of 50mm with a "clean" material which will suppress the weeds and help to retain the soil moisture. Another advantage is that a mulch improves the appearance of a bed particularly in winter.

Compost is not always readily available but its high nutrient content is a bonus. Bark mulch has become popular in recent years. Care must be taken in specification to avoid resinous and possible disease infested bark, and both sphagnum and sedge peats can be used. They are best if applied at the end of the growing period. Lime may be added to adjust the pH value and it is good practice to fork the peat in at springtime.

In addition, shrub beds require pruning, fertiliser application especially in spring, watering and replacement planting.

REFERENCES AND FURTHER READING

BRITISH STANDARDS INSTITUTION. General landscape operations. BSI, London, 1969, BS4428.

HACKETT B. Landscape planning. Oriel Press, Henley-on-Thames, 1971.

LOVEJOY D. (Ed.). Land use and landscape planning. Leonard Hill Books, London, 1973.

TANDY C. Handbook of urban landscape. Architectural Press, London, 1978.

TANDY C. Landscape of industry. Leonard Hill Books, London, 1975.

THOMAS G.S. Plant for ground cover. J.M. Dent & Sons Ltd, London, 1977 (revised edition).

Address: The Soil Survey of England and Wales,
            Rothamstead Experimental Station, Harpenden,
            Hertfordshire AL5 2JQ.

Chapter 8

GROUND ENGINEERING

INTRODUCTION

Ground conditions are a key factor when considering the technical and economic aspects of any construction project. The objectives of the ground investigation are to obtain relevant information on the engineering properties of the ground and to provide practical advice on the various elements of ground related construction involved in both site preparation and building design.

Each site is unique and some require specialist advice. This section endeavours to cover, broadly, three main areas relating to ground engineering: site preparation, stability of mineral workings and contamination.

SITE PREPARATION

Demolition

Planning consent for demolition is not required, although it is advisable that notice of intent be given to the planning authority to allow it the opportunity to comment. In Scotland, notice is required under building control regulations.

Demolition should be undertaken with care and consideration of after-use. Where services crossing a site have to be retained, it is important that these are identified to the contractor and the mode of protection specified. The temptation to remove only the superstructure, the lucrative aspect of demolition, should be avoided. The credit element of this section of work should be used to help fund the removal of underground structures or provide cover to these obstructions.

Consideration should be given to crusher plant on site to recover clean demolition material[hardcore] for reuse, particularly in areas where hardcore is not readily available or expensive.

Health and safety aspects in demolition work are of a paramount importance and should be observed at all times; and the control and disposal of dangerous substances such as asbestos and toxic waste should be set out in the contract document with the working method stipulated. Reference to BS 6187 : 1981 Demoliton, is advised.

Financial assistance for the clearance of industrial dereliction is available from government departments in the UK although the method of funding varies regionally.

ELEMENTS OF CONSTRUCTION

Earthworks

A number of elements of construction listed below will be encountered during the development of a site. The ground investigation as discussed in Chapter five will have provided the necessary information to allow economic design of these items.

Gradients of slopes can vary in ratio from near vertical to 1:5 requiring assessment to ensure stability. It is possible that some form of earth retention may be required and the possibility of crib walling or gabions should be examined together with reinforced concrete retaining walls.

The ground investigations should also be geared to provide information which will allow assessment of temporary works such as trenching and also the stability of services, drainage and roadworks.

Industrial development generally leads to the need to prepare large building platforms. This is achieved by lowering or raising the levels of the site using cut or fill techniques.

Sites which have already been filled require careful examination in order to ensure that the fill materials and the method of placement is suitable for the development proposed. New fill can be more readily controlled and it is recommended that the Department of Transport specification for roads and bridge works is used to control the selection and placing of fill materials.

Where it is possible the design team should seek to balance earthworks quantities involved with cut and fill. However, tests are required in order to ensure that the cut material can be reused. Surplus material can be used in nonstructural areas, such as landscaping, or be hauled to a suitable tip.

Where importation of fill is necessary, short haul borrow pit sites will have to be found. The economics of hauling quantities of fill material to the site will have to be evaluated; along with ground investigation at the borrow pit site to establish suitability of the proposed fill material.

Groundwater

Groundwater is one of the most significant influences on ground engineering. It is advisable to install methods of measurement and systems for monitoring behaviour during the predesign and design stages of a project where groundwater exists.

The technical team should be aware when diverting or culverting a water course and making it an integral part of the site surface water drainage system it could consequently negate the adoption of part or all of the system by the sewerage authority.

Water tables can vary greatly with site conditions and it is important to monitor any fluctuations in level and the pore water pressure. This will help the design team decide whether pumping might be required during excavation or if a specialist method of dewatering might be necessary. Note: Reducing local water tables for prolonged periods can cause shrinkage, with consequent damage to neighbouring foundations and vegetation.

Another problem can be the inadvertant creation of artesian wells by tapping water bound strata under a head of water while driving a borehole.

The ground investigation should have identified the chemical properties of the under water in order to determine the best selection of construction materials.

Foundations

The type of foundations for building vary according to ground conditions and can be summarised as follows:

- Pad and strip footings where competent ground conditions exist, or are provided by some form of ground treatment in advance

- Ring beam and independent floor slabs where there is adequate but variable bearing capacity

- Edge beams and integrated floor slabs [rafts] where the bearing capacity is approaching the inadequate and variable, and there is a need to distribute foundation loads over the building area

- End bearing piles and friction piles where the bearing capacity is inadequate and loads must be transferred to a competent bearing strata

- Newer techniques such as geotextiles and earth reinforcement can deal with certain ground water and weak soil conditions.

Ground treatment

Again there is a wide variety of ground treatment methods available to the design team. These can involve:

- Reconsolidation entailing excavation and recompaction of existing weak ground

- Surcharging by means of uniformly loading the existing ground to accelerate settlement to that anticipated by proposed building loads

- Dynamic compaction involving repeated surface tamping using a heavy weight of 10t – 20t freefalling up to 25 m to improve the bearing capacities of large areas of filled ground

- Vibro-compaction/replacement techniques using depth vibrators which with the employment of air or water under pressure create vertical holes in the ground. These vertical holes are infilled with granualar material which is compacted with the vibrator to provide improved support to structures without excessive settlement

- Infilling of voids within soils and rocks by pressure grouting to control ground movement

- Jet grouting and chemical application are new techniques which are being studied at present and could prove successful in the future.

Different types of foundation and ground improvement methods can be combined to provide an economical solution to a developer's problem [for instance, a raft foundation on vibro-compacted ground].

MINERAL STABILITY

Background

The extraction of underlying minerals can seriously affect the structural stability of any site both in the short- and long-term. Coal is probably the mineral first thought of in such a context but may others such as iron, salt, fireclay lead, tin and so on must not be overlooked. The methods of extraction for each mineral vary but all involve removal of material [and therefore support] from below the surface of the ground; and the gaining of access by means of vertical shafts or sloping adits. Sudden collapses of the ground surface still occur where access to old working was gained by means of vertical shafts or sloping adits in the days before accurate records were maintained.

Methods of extraction

Prior to 1872 there was no legal requirement for owners of coalmines and so on to maintain accurate records of extraction. Although over 70 000 old workings have been traced and recorded, it is thought probable that another 30 000 exist together with a large number of shafts. The result is that a considerable lack of information exists about surface stability in mining areas.

The original method of 'bell pit' mining which prevailed between 13th and 16th centuries was gradually replaced by more general systems of extraction involving ever-increasing depths as pumping, winding, haulage and ventilation improved. These methods involved either:

- Partial extraction which left pillars of coal behind to support the ground above

- Total extraction known as the longwall method which allows complete removal of the coal seam between tunnel headings.

Old shafts associated with access and ventilation have generally been inadequately infilled. Often a timber platform was installed at a convenient level with an open shaft left below and loose fill above. Their exact location is now extremely difficult to re-establish.

Virtually all old workings are prone to collapse and require detailed investigation to suit the design life and complexity of the structure to be erected on the surface. In the case of partial extraction the pillars of coal will continue to deteriorate over a time-scale of hundreds of years with a probable uneven subsidence of the surface and the sudden appearance of large cavities. Current methods of extraction are such that surface movement follows closely behind as a general rule, although as the support of the main access roads are frequently retained, settlements between these roads can be uneven.

Mineshafts also present a serious danger and all should be regarded as potentially unstable. Even where a shaft has been completely filled, fines in the fill may migrate along old workings causing large voids; voids can also be caused during filling as a result of the material lodging on projections and arcing over; full compaction of the fill is rarely possible and later variation in ground water levels can result in settlement of varying magnitude. In addition, all linings - be they timber, cast iron, brick or concrete - will eventually decay and fall away. Consequently it is rarely advisable to erect any structure within a 9m radius of the shaft, or such other increased radius that may be considered advisable after taking into account the particular geology of the site and the type of structure.

Another form of extraction of minerals is the opencast method which has been carried out for many years during which time equipment has increased greatly in size and depth or thickness of overburden has similarly increased. This has a significant impact on the bearing capacity of the reinstated overburden materials. It has been generally assumed that 20 years was more than adequate for less sensitive types of structures to ensure adequate settlement had occurred before building construction.

However, recent research has shown that this empirical rule only applies to sites where the natural groundwater level has been quickly re-established. Problems have been experienced with those sites where the natural ground water level has been artificially kept low for a number of years before being allowed to rise to its natural level. In such cases secondary settlements of 1.5% of the depth of fill can be expected.

Investigation

Land which has been subjected to mineral extraction should be carefully investigated. Initial information can be obtained from:

- The Mineral Valuer [government and local authorities only]
- British Geological Survey or Geological Survey, Northern Ireland
- National Coal Board - which has very detailed records of all recent workings.

If there is still a risk that future collapse could occur then borings will be necessary which should be carried out under the direct control of an experienced mining engineer.

Treatment of old workings

There are five main ways of dealing with a site which has been subjected to previous workings and where surface stability is considered inadequate for the expected life or type of proposed structure:

- Selection of a structure type designed to accommodate differential movement

- Incorporation of methods of relevelling the structure

- Design of foundations to allow for isolated withdrawal of support in certain areas

- Stabilisation of the site by employment of grouting techniques

- Rejection of the site.

If the stabilisation by grouting is accepted, it should be appreciated that it is not an exact science on account of the uncertain records and information available. It is possible that the final cost can be many times more than that originally estimated with - for example - extensive loss of grout into old mine workings. In view of this type of problem, it is essential that the best of consultants' advice is employed.

Treatment of open cast sites

Open cast sites should again be the subject of a very detailed investigation to establish the limits of the boundaries of the excavation, method of working, details of natural groundwater and other information which will allow the assessment of potential future settlement. Piling could be considered through to the pit bottom if significant settlement has to be avoided.

CONTAMINATED LAND

Land which has been contaminated by past industrial use has only relatively recently been recognised as presenting significant redevelopment problems. There have been occasions when significant problems have been completely overlooked with resulting serious delays in construction activities which have already started on site.

There is a wide range of sites which have been in former industrial use and could have a significant contamination problem. Apart from the visually obvious chemical tips, difficulties are experienced with former gas works, electrical capacitor manufacture; tanneries and gelatine works, metal production and recycling; oil tanks and sewage treatment works.

Investigation

The history of any site should be investigated in order to check whether it might have been contaminated as a result of a previous use. This investigation should be carried out prior to any activities such as demolition or adjustment to levels in order to avoid spreading possible contamination throughout the site.

The investigation would normally take the form of trial pitting under experienced supervision. Boreholes may also be required where contaminants are at a deeper level and could move in the ground water.

Methane gas can also present fire and toxic hazards and samples should be taken in order to determine the presence of this gas in areas such as refuse tips.

Methane can exist naturally on sites situated over coal measures with shafts and adits present for example. Based on the results of the investigation, precautions can be taken to eliminate or at least minimise the risk of methane gas. This can be best achieved by one or a combination of the following approaches:

- Further compaction of the site reducing the percentage voids that carry the gas and stopping the migration of air [oxygen] to the gas which increases the risk of spontaneous combustion

- Venting the layer to the atmosphere by the placement of stone columns - vibro compaction method - before providing an inert air-tight layer under the building area

- Suspended floor with under slab ventilation.

End use

The end use of a site is the determining factor on the extent of the necessary remedial works required. Housing with gardens is the most sensitive use which can involve direct contact with the soil by children and uptake of chemicals via vegetables and so on. Areas accessible to the public, such as playgrounds, form the next most sensitive use, but industrial, commercial or domestic developments which have little or no accessible soft landscaping are generally the most acceptable to the authorities.

However, it must always be borne in mind that the construction workforce will be in contact with the contamination whatever the end use and the most stringent of safety precautions must be carried out from the word go. It is also important that the effect of contaminants on foundations and all underground services be established.

Remedial works

The effect of disturbance on the current chemical regime of the site must be considered. Care must be taken to ensure that the necessary remedial works do not result in migration of contamination from the site to affect adjoining areas or watercourses. In practical terms removal of identified ´hot spot´ areas is effective. Wholescale removal of contamination for the site is likely to be uneconomical particularly as there will be a shortage of tips to accept such material.

The remaining material can either be carefully transferred to a designated area within the site or covered using clean material. Whatever technique is adopted the full implications of the contaminants remaining on the site have to be considered from the health, plant growth and construction materials aspects.

REFERENCES AND FURTHER READING

BARRY D.L. Redevelopment - the significance of contamination. Environmental Consultancy - Atkins Research and Development, 1982.

BRITISH STANDARDS INSTITUTION. Demolition. BSI, London, 1981, BS 6187.

CHARLES J.A., NAISMITH W.A and BURFORD D. Settlement of backfill at Horsley restored open cast coal mining site. Proceedings of conference on large ground movements and structures at University of Wales Institute of Science and Technology. Pentech Press, London, 1977, July, 229-251.

CHARLES J. A., HUGHES D.B. and BURFORD D. The effect of a rise of water table on the settlement of backfill at Horsley restored open cast coal mining site, 1973-1983. Proceedings of 3rd International Conference on ground movements and structures at University of Wales Institute of Science and Technology. Pentech Press, London, 1984, July.

HEALY P.R. and HEAD J.M. Construction over abandoned mine workings. Construction Industry Research & Information Association. Special Publication 32, London, 1984. Property Services Agency Civil Engineering Technical Guide 34.

KILKENNY W.M. A study of the settlement of restored open cast coal sites and their stability for building development. University of Newcastle upon Tyne, Department of Civil Engineering, 1968, May.

LITTLEJOHN G.S. Surface stability in areas underlain by old coal workings. J. Ground Engineering, 1979, March.

MARSH J.V. and THOMSON G.H. Ground Treatment. Proc. Instn Civ. Engrs, Part 1, 1982, 72, Aug., 487-489 (Informal Discussion).

SMYTH-OSBOURNE K.R. Settlement of a factory on open cast backfill. Proceedings of 3rd International Conference on Ground Movements and Structures, University of Wales Institute of Science and Technology. Pentech Press, London, 1984, July.

Chapter 9

HIGHWAYS

INTRODUCTION

The layout and construction standards of roads in industrial and commercial areas are generally subject to the approval of the local highway authority. Experience has shown that such standards can vary considerably from authority to authority and their interpretation from one officer to another within the same office.

The objective of this chapter is to provide guidance on the desirable standards which should be adopted for roads in industrial and commercial areas. It should be borne in mind, however, that early contact with the local highway authority is essential to discuss the proposed scheme, preferably with the officer from whom approval will eventually be sought.

Traffic generation

Data sources covering traffic generation from industrial estates were found during research for this document to be 10 years old or more and to relate principally to England. Little research had been carried out with Scotland, Wales and Northern Ireland. In addition, studies which were available had been of an academic nature where the researchers were attempting to explain all variations in traffic flows, with few practical guidelines for estate planners.

In order to obtain reliable information a consultant was commissioned to carry out a traffic survey at industrial estates throughout the United Kingdom. Full details of this survey are contained in the report 'Industrial and commercial estate traffic generation' which is available as a separate document [see References to Ch. Six.].

A total of 58 estates were surveyed during September to November 1983. Of this total 21 estates were in England, 14 in Scotland, 13 in Wales and 10 in Northern Ireland. The selection of the sites was designed to ensure that a representative sample of estates was surveyed nationally and their location is shown in Fig. 12. In all, 38,000 roadside interviews were held during the survey.

The most important element of the study was the roadside interview survey which used a simple and direct interview technique. This gave information relating to source of traffic generation from each

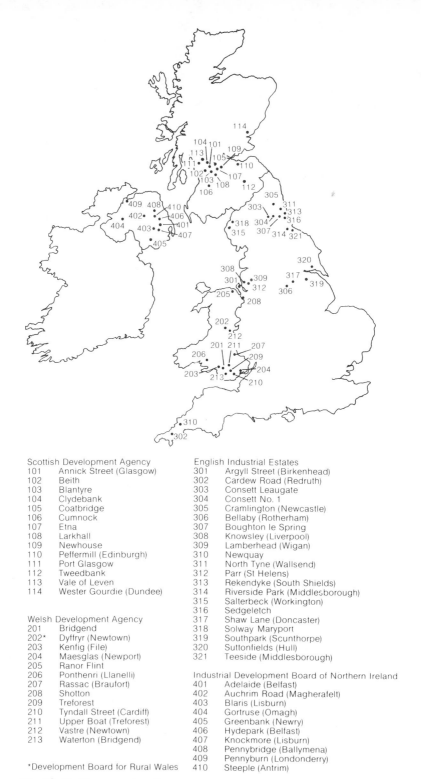

Scottish Development Agency
101 Annick Street (Glasgow)
102 Beith
103 Blantyre
104 Clydebank
105 Coatbridge
106 Cumnock
107 Etna
108 Larkhall
109 Newhouse
110 Peffermill (Edinburgh)
111 Port Glasgow
112 Tweedbank
113 Vale of Leven
114 Wester Gourdie (Dundee)

Welsh Development Agency
201 Bridgend
202* Dyffryr (Newtown)
203 Kenfig (File)
204 Maesglas (Newport)
205 Ranor Flint
206 Ponthenri (Llanelli)
207 Rassac (Braufort)
208 Shotton
209 Treforest
210 Tyndall Street (Cardiff)
211 Upper Boat (Treforest)
212 Vastre (Newtown)
213 Waterton (Bridgend)

*Development Board for Rural Wales

English Industrial Estates
301 Argyll Street (Birkenhead)
302 Cardew Road (Redruth)
303 Consett Leaugate
304 Consett No. 1
305 Cramlington (Newcastle)
306 Bellaby (Rotherham)
307 Boughton le Spring
308 Knowsley (Liverpool)
309 Lamberhead (Wigan)
310 Newquay
311 North Tyne (Wallsend)
312 Parr (St Helens)
313 Rekendyke (South Shields)
314 Riverside Park (Middlesborough)
315 Salterbeck (Workington)
316 Sedgeletch
317 Shaw Lane (Doncaster)
318 Solway Maryport
319 Southpark (Scunthorpe)
320 Suttonfields (Hull)
321 Teeside (Middlesborough)

Industrial Development Board of Northern Ireland
401 Adelaide (Belfast)
402 Auchrim Road (Magherafelt)
403 Blaris (Lisburn)
404 Gortruse (Omagh)
405 Greenbank (Newry)
406 Hydepark (Belfast)
407 Knockmore (Lisburn)
408 Pennybridge (Ballymena)
409 Pennyburn (Londonderry)
410 Steeple (Antrim)

Fig. 12. Traffic survey locations

individual estate. Volumetric counts were also carried out on the
estate access road and parking surveys were undertaken at selected
times throughout the day to determine the location and extent of
parked traffic. Further information was collected on employment on
the site, and floor areas and details of business undertaken at each
firm.

All data were collated and examined by the consultant. Various
factors were found to influence the numbers and types of trip
generation, for example, employment levels, type of industry and
activity, location of estate [urban, suburban or rural], male/female
employee ratios and size of firm. Analysis of the data indicated
that employment figures gave a more reliable trip generation level
than did factory floor areas.

It was therefore recommended that trip generation prediction should
be based on expected employment levels. Coefficients were derived
from the survey data which could be applied to the different
variables influencing trip generation levels. The data are
presented, analyses are described and conclusions are justified in
the consultant's report. Armed with these conclusions, it is possible
to predict total daily trip generation and peak hourly trip
generation for each type of trip category [that is, car work, car
business, car other and goods vehicle]. "Industrial and commercial
estate traffic generation" provides the designer with a methodology
to compare the effects and costs of varying the design standards.

ROAD TYPES

Each local highway authority has the responsibility of traffic
management, maintenance and development control in its own area.
Roads are classified depending on their function, with each type
having its place in a road hierarchy. The nomenclature and
definition of road types vary between authorities. However, in
general four main types of road can be identified:

-    Primary distributors/principal roads/trunk roads: Roads which form
the main links in the national or regional traffic system or between
large towns, cities or industrial areas. They will generally carry
through traffic with a large proportion of heavy goods vehicles

-    District distributors/class B roads/main roads: Roads which
distribute traffic between residential, industrial and principal
business districts of a town or form main rural routes between towns

-    Local distributors/class C roads: Roads which distribute traffic
within environmental areas or link those areas to district
distributors. They also act as a link between villages or on to the
main road network

-    Access roads/unclassified roads: Roads which give direct access to individual buildings or groups of buildings. They can take the form of long lengths or rural road or in the urban setting short lengths of residential street.

It is into such an hierarchal system that the roads of any proposed industrial development will be introduced and eventually, when constructed and adopted, become part. It is important at the outset to establish the classification of existing highways adjoining and leading to the proposed development; and to find out if any restrictions or obligations are to be placed on the proposed estate roads [for example, to carry heavy through traffic or form part of a one way system]. Local distributor and access roads require further definition to suit industrial development.

Local distributor roads distribute traffic to different zones within the estate and have limited frontage access.

Access roads fall into three categories:

- Major access roads which have frequent frontage accesses to premises but with sufficient space inside plots to allow all movements on and off the road to be in a forward direction

- Minor access roads that serve a smaller number of premises so that closely spaced accesses can be allowed with some reversing movements on the roads

- Service roads which serve a small group of premises with virtually continuous access and provision for manoeuvring on the road.

A typical estate road hierarchy is shown in Fig. 13.

ADOPTION OF ROADS

The developer is relieved of the responsibility for the maintenance of the roads and footpaths, grass cutting on the verges, service of street lighting and provision of traffic signs and roadmarkings if a road is adopted by the highway authority. The highway authority is also responsible for the indemnification against injury to pedestrians and drivers on publicly adopted roads. Roads carrying scheduled bus services or to be subject to parking restrictions should be adopted in order to avoid legal complications associated with these activities. It should also be borne in mind that the developer is relieved of substantial future maintenance costs if the roads are adopted.

However, the benefits of adoption have to be weighed against the fact that the required adoption standards can be costly for certain types of development and may be considered unnecessary. The timing of adoption will vary depending on the progress of development and future flexibility. In any event a cost/benefit exercise should be carried out before decisions are reached on whether or not to adopt.

Any road to be offered for adoption must be designed and constructed to standards acceptable to the highway authority. All adoption formalities should be complete and approval received before construction commences. It is possible to arrange adoption of existing roads although further construction or repair work might be required on them before they are accepted.

It is likely that the highway authority will require the facility to inspect the works as they proceed. This inspection can vary from occasional visits up to full supervision which might cost up to 5% of the contract value. This cost can be minimised if the highway authority accepts self-certification by the chartered civil engineer in charge of the road construction.

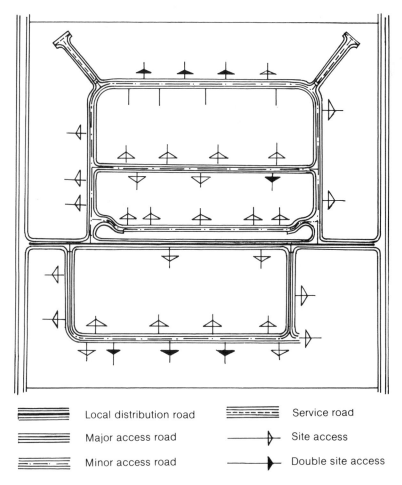

≡≡≡≡≡	Local distribution road	≡≡≡≡≡	Service road
≡≡≡≡≡	Major access road	——▷—	Site access
≡≡≡≡≡	Minor access road	——▶—	Double site access

Fig. 13. Estate road hierarchy — notional layout for an estate of about 40 hectares

The relevant certificate should be obtained from the highway authority on satisfactory completion of the construction work; and after the maintenance period [normally 12 months] full adoption should be requested.

STANDARDS

Design speed

The design speed for access and service roads should be 30mph; with 40mph used for local distributor roads. The design speed of traffic using existing roads at the entrances to estates should be established since this determines the layout and could dictate the location of the entrance. ´Sleeping policemen´ type features may be necessary where very low speeds are desired.

Widths

The recommended road widths for industrial estates are shown in Table 6.

Table 6. Road widths

Road Type	Carriageway width
Local distributor	7.3 – 9.0 metres
Major access road	7.3 mteres
Minor access road	6.0 – 7.3 metres
Service road	6.0 metres or less
One way road [with passing bays]	4.0 metres
Footpaths	1.8 metres
Grass verges	2.0 metres

Only if the estate road forms part of a larger regional road system with heavy traffic should consideration be given to the provision of dual carriageways. Short lengths or 9m wide road or dual carriageway could be provided at the entrances to larger estates to allow contraflow or lane stacking.

Road cross-section

Fig. 14 illustrates a recommended road cross-section for industrial estates. Footpaths should be separated from the carriageway by a 2m verge to increase pedestrian safety. Lamp standards are located at the back of the verges to minimise risk of impact.

Turning circles occupy a considerable space and their provision must be considered at the early planning stages. Fig. 15 shows three types of turning facilities suitable for publicly adopted roads. Where possible, entrances could be incorporated in a turning head or bay and should be discussed with the highway authority. Footpaths and verges should be carried round the turning facility. If the estate road system is being developed in phases, temporary turning areas may be incorporated as required.

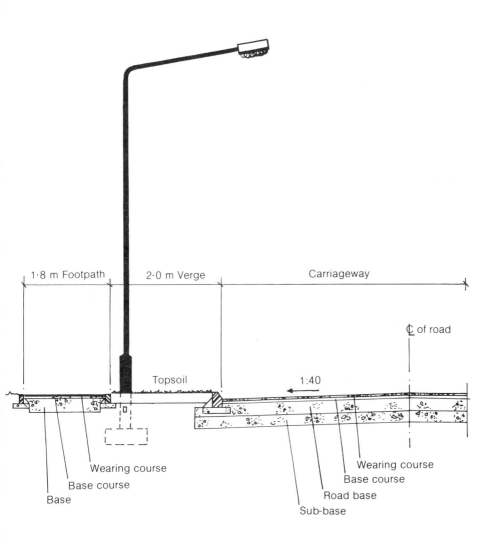

1·8 m Footpath   2·0 m Verge   Carriageway

₵ of road

Topsoil   1:40

Wearing course
Base course
Base

Wearing course
Base course
Road base
Sub-base

Fig. 14. Road cross-section

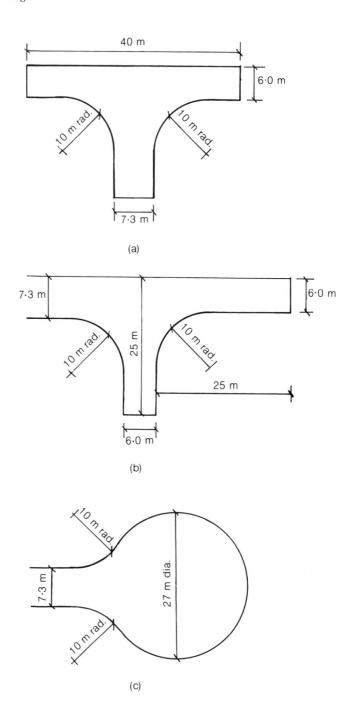

Fig. 15. Turning heads: (a) hammer-head; (b) alternative turning head; (c) turning circle

Gradients

Only in special circumstances and for short lengths should gradients steeper than 1:15 be contemplated. Gradients between 1:20 and 1:25 should be considered a maximum for estate roads while gradients of less than 1:100 might require concrete channels and double gullies to deal with surface water. At road junctions the gradient of the road joining the main road is restricted to 1:30 for a distance of 10m from the junction.

Visibility

The recommended sight splays required for estate road junctions are given in Table 7.

Table 7. Junction visibility

SPEED OF TRAFFIC ON THE MAJOR ROAD	The first figure given for the x or y distance is the normal and the figure in brackets is the minimum and is only used in special circumstances at the discretion of the highway authority.							
	MAJOR ACCESSES			MINOR ACCESSES			SINGLE OR PAIRED ACCESSES	
	Main route	Secondary route	Other routes	Main route	Secondary routes	Other routes	Main route	Secondary and other routes
	'X' 'Y' m	'X' 'Y' m	'X' 'Y' m	'X' 'Y' m	'X' 'Y' m	'X' 'Y' m	'X' 'Y' m	'X' 'Y' m
Above 50 mph	9 220	9 220	6 180	6 220 [4]	5 180 [3]	5 180 [3]	2.4 180 [125]	2.4 125
50 mph	9 150	9 150	5 100	6 150 [4]	5 130 [3]	5 100 [3]	2.4 100 [70]	2.4 100 [70]
40 mph	9 120	6 120	5 80	6 120 [4]	5 90 [3]	5 80 [2.4]	2.4 80 [60]	2.4 80 [45]
30 mph & under	9 90	5 90	5 60	5 90 [3]	5 60 [3]	5 60 [2.4]	2.4 60 [40]	2.4 60 [30]

The sight line requirements should be applied to cover the reasonably expected speed of traffic using the road.

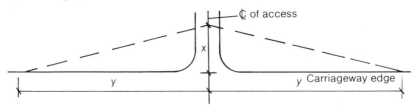

The distance x is measured along the centre line of the access for the continuation of the line of the near edge of the carriageway of the road.

The y distance is measured along the nearer edge of the carriageway from its intersection with the centre line of the access as shown in the diagram above.

All sight lines, vertical and horizontal, are based on a line of sight of 1.05m [3ft 6 in.] above the carriageway.

Sight distances, both vertical and horizontal, not associated with junctions should be measured between points of the centre line of both the near side and off side lanes of the carriageway. The minimum overtaking and stopping distances are recommended in Table 8 with a reminder that landscape, street furniture and so on, must not obstruct sight lines of horizontal curves.

Table 8. Sight distances

Design speed m.p.h.	Sight distances Minimum overtaking distance [single carriageway] m	Sight distances Minimum stopping distance [single & dual carriageways] m
50	360	140
40	270	90
30	225	70
20	135	30

Spacing of junctions

The recommended minimum spacings for road junctions and accesses are shown in the diagram below and Table 9. Recommended kerb radii at junctions are shown in Table 10.

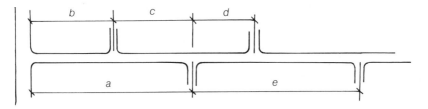

Table 9. Junction spacing

Distance in metres	Local distributor	Access roads	
		Major	Minor & service
a. Distance to first junction from major road, RH side	80 to 120	50	40
b. Distance to first junctions from major road, LH side	50 to 60	40	25
c. Junction spacing opposite LH stagger	40 to 60	25	20
d. Junction spacing opposite RH stagger	40	20	20
e. Junction spacing adjacent	80 to 120	40	40

Table 10. Kerb radii

Road type	Junction width	Kerb radius [m]
Local distributor Major access road	Existing roads Local distributor Major access road	10 - 12.5
Minor access road	Existing roads Local distributor	10
Service road	Major access road	8
	Minor Access Road	6

Horizontal curves and superelevation

The degree of superelevation which is applied to a curve should be
kept to a minimum. A superelevation of 1:24 should be regarded as
desirable and in no case should it be steeper than 1:14.5 or flatter
than the standard carriageway crossfall. Adverse camber should be
eliminated with superelevation introduced where necessary.

Horizontal radii should, where applicable, be kept to a maximum.
Depending on design speed the desirable minimum radius is 300m and the
absolute minimum about 90m. Transition curves should be incorporated
at the ends of curves and if necessary with width of road on the curve
should be increased to smooth the transition.

Vertical curves should be provided at all changes in gradient along
the length of a road. The characteristics of the curve can be
calucated using the formula $L = KA$ where

L = length of curve [metres]
A = algebraic difference of gradients [%]
and K = value selected from Table 11

Table 11. Minimum vertical curves

DESIGN SPEED	MINIMUM K VALUE FOR STOPPING AND COMFORT	MINIMUM VERTICAL CURVE LENGTH
mph		metres
50	25	50
40	10	40
30	6	30
20	1	20

Crossfalls

The following crossfalls are recommended:-

- Roads: between 1:40 and 1:48 or in cases of steep gradients
  or need to increase a rate of run-off: 1:30

- Footpaths: a minimum of 1:40 towards the verge

- Grass verge: 1:20 towards the carriageway.

Sideslopes of embankments and cuttings should be designed at a maximum of 1:2. For heights greater than 2m, sideslopes of 1:3 should be considered. These slopes may need to be modified to suit local ground conditions and to enable maintenance as discussed in the landscaping chapter.

Street lighting

Street lighting is designed in accordance with BS5489 [formerly CP1004], parts two and three which covers groups A and B lighting. Lighting columns should be to BS5649.

Generally the street lighting section of the highway authority will be willing to carry out a complete lighting scheme for an estate if provided with a copy of the proposed layout. This is useful particularly if the estate roads are to be adopted.

Lighting columns should be situated at least 2m from the carriageway at the back of the grass verge or footpath as appropriate.

The policy of highway authorities towards payment for street lighting varies but in Scotland street lighting can be provided free of charge, by the authority.

Traffic signs and road markings

These are generally the responsibility of the highway authority although the developer is likely to bear the initial provision costs.

Safety fences

Safety fences should be provided on corners when the estate road is on embankments of appreciable height.

Street furniture

Street furniture such as street nameplates, water main valve posts, telephone control boxes, seating and so on should be located at least 2m back from the edge of the carriageway at the back of the footpath or verge. They must also be located so as not to obstruct sightlines.

Duct markers

The location of service ducts where they cross the highway should be marked by either colour coded timber posts, or more permanently by double kerbs or markings cut on kerbs.

Structures

Where a structure associated with a river, railway or road is required, the relevant authorities must be consulted early on to establish design criteria, responsibility and maintenance commitments. Early contact should be made with the public utilities in order to ensure that services can be accommodated within the overall design of the structure. It is also possible that the public utilities might be interested in contributing towards part of the cost of structures in order to obtain additional space for their own general requirements.

Generally, independent design checks are required for all structures associated with highways including culverts, retaining walls as well as bridges. Special procedures such as obtaining approval from the Railway Inspectorate for bridges over railways must be borne in mind at the time of preparing the development programme.

CONSTRUCTION

Transport & Road Research Laboratory "Road Note 29" or LR1132 should be used as a basis to determine the depth of construction of an estate road based on information obtained from the ground investigation and anticipated traffic flows. The specification recommended is the Department of Transport specification for roads and bridge works.

The type of wearing surfaces normally provided in industrial estates can vary but the most common is hot rolled asphalt. Concrete or paviors are an alternative and could be particularly valuable in areas where spillage of fuel can be expected. The effect of heavy vehicle manoeuvring can require a higher standard of surfacing.

Paviors should comply with the requirements of the Cement & Concrete Association/County Surveyors Society/Interpave Specification – September 1980, and be laid in accordance with code of practice for laying precast concrete block pavements – February 1983.

Concrete pavements should be designed and constructed in accordance with "A guide to concrete road construction" published by Her Majesty's Stationery Office.

REFERENCES AND FURTHER READING

BORDERS REGIONAL COUNCIL. Common standards for design and construction of new private roadworks being constructed with the intention of subsequently being added to the appropriate list of highways.

CENTRAL REGIONAL COUNCIL. Geometric standards and specification for roads.

ESSEX COUNTY COUNCIL. Design guide for residential areas.

GATESHEAD METROPOLITAN BOROUGH. Standard construction details for highways.

GRAMPIAN REGIONAL COUNCIL. Geometric and construction standards for maintainable highways.

MIDDLESBOROUGH BOROUGH COUNCIL. Specification and design criteria for privately developed estates.

NORTHUMBERLAND COUNTY COUNCIL. Manual on the design and construction of estate roads.

NORTH YORKSHIRE COUNTY COUNCIL. Specification for housing and industrial estate roads and private streetworks.

POWYS COUNTY COUNCIL. Design standards for layout of estate roads.

STRATHCLYDE DEPARTMENT OF ROADS. Guidelines for development roads.

TAYSIDE REGIONAL COUNCIL. Road standards.

TYNE AND WEAR COUNTY COUNCIL. Design and construction of roads and accesses to adoptable standards.

BRITISH STANDARDS INSTITUTION. A and B lighting. BSI, London, BS 5489 (formerly CP1004), Parts 2 and 3.

BRITISH STANDARDS INSTITUTION. Lighting columns. BSI, London, BSI 5649.

CEMENT AND CONCRETE ASSOCIATION/COUNTY SURVEYORS' SOCIETY/INTERPAVE. Specification for Precast concrete paving blocks. Published jointly by the Cement and Concrete Association, the County Surveyors' Society and the Interlocking Paving Association (Interpave), 1980, Sept.

DEPARTMENT OF THE ENVIRONMENT FOR NORTHERN IRELAND. Layout of new streets.

DEPARTMENT OF THE ENVIRONMENT FOR NORTHERN IRELAND. Access standards.

DEPARTMENT OF THE ENVIRONMENT, SCOTTISH DEVELOPMENT DEPARTMENT, THE WELSH OFFICE. Roads in urban areas. HMSO, London.

DEPARTMENT OF THE ENVIRONMENT, SCOTTISH DEVELOPMENT DEPARTMENT, THE WELSH OFFICE. Layout of roads in rural areas, HMSO, London.

DEVELOPMENT BOARD FOR RURAL WALES. Design guidance notes.

DEVELOPMENT BOARD FOR RURAL WALES. Standard construction details.

HADFIELD W. Designing for deliveries - design standards for services and off-street loading areas. Freight Transport Association Ltd, Tunbridge Wells, 1972.

JAMIESON MACKAY AND PARTERNS: Scottish Development Agency. Industrial and commercial estate traffic generation. Part 1: Surveys and analysis; Part 2: Procedures for estimating traffic generation. Reports prepared for Joint Technical Committee. Thomas Telford Limited, London, 1985.

POWELL W.D. et al. The structural design of bituminous roads. Transport and Road Research Laboratory, Crowthorne, 1984, LR 1132.

ROAD RESEARCH LABORATORY. A guide to the structural design of pavements for new roads. Road Note 29, HMSO, London, 1970, 3rd edn.

Chapter 10

PUBLIC UTILITIES

INTRODUCTION

The object of site development is to provide the essential services
which are necessary for a building to function. Services must be
conveniently located adjacent to the boundaries of building plots
where site development is carried out in advance of building works.
Where plots have not been defined, the servicing process may be
limited to the more general provision of mains. The servicing of a
site normally involves the provision of new off-site works or the
reinforcement of an existing system, with both cost and programme
implications.

The development of the site demands the identification, location and
assessment of a variety of overhead and underground mains and services
which may impinge on the proposed development. Such apparatus may
have to be removed, diverted or altered to accommodate the development
or may require amendments to the site layout. Cost and programme
effects of this will have to be taken into account.

DEFINITION OF PUBLIC UTILITIES AND ASSOCIATED APPARATUS

The term "public utilities" is used to encompass those authorities
which are responsible for providing the basic services of gas,
electricity, water, telecommunications and drainage to the community.
Most of these services are provided by the utility boards themselves
under various forms of financial arrangement. Sewers, by contrast,
are normally constructed by the developer although they may be offered
to the sewerage authority for adoption.

The legal powers and duties of public utilities differ throughout the
United Kingdom, being generally identical within England and Wales but
with Scotland and Northern Ireland having their own individual
systems. The legal position regarding public utility apparatus laid
in public highways is defined in various Acts, the most important
being the Public Utilities Street Works Act 1950 - England, Wales and
Scotland - and the Private Streets [Northern Ireland] Order 1980.

Under the Gas Act 1972 it is the duty of the Gas Corporation to
develop and maintain an efficient, co-ordinated and economical system
of gas supply for Great Britain. The corporation is empowered to
purchase compulsorily any land, including any easement or right over

land, which is required for or in connection with the exercise or performance of its functions. A request for information on gas apparatus is normally directed to the regional gas authority and results in the internal gathering of information from the transmission and distribution departments.

The generation and distribution of electricity is the responsibility of several authorities dependent upon location. In both Scotland and Northern Ireland the generating and distribution functions are combined under the appropriate regional board. In England and Wales electricity is generated by the Central Electricity Generating Board and distributed by area boards under the Electricity Act 1947. Both area and generating boards are empowered to purchase compulsorily any land required to carry out their functions or may purchase an easement or right to place apparatus in land. The initial location or diversion of any overhead electricity line requires planning consent and in certain circumstances the consent of the Secretary of State.

The Water Act 1973 and the Water & Sewerage Services [Northern Ireland] Order 1973 set up regional water authorities. In Scotland, regional local authorities are responsible for the supply of potable water. Statutory Water Companies can remain in existence and continue to supply water outside its limits of supply by agreement. Express planning permission is not required for the laying of underground mains, pipes or other apparatus. Where the authority wishes to lay a main in private land the consent of every owner and occupier must be obtained and this consent cannot unreasonably be withheld. The authority has power to acquire land by agreement or compulsorily with the consent of the Secretary of State. This includes any interest, right or easement in, to or over land.

Responsibility for sewerage and sewage disposal, prevention of pollution and the supervision of land drainage varies throughout the United Kingdom. In England and Wales the water authorities cover all aspects while in Scotland and Northern Ireland separate organisations deal with the control of pollution in water courses. The authority responsible for sewerage has a duty to provide such public sewers as may be necessary for effectively draining its area and for effectively dealing with the contents of the sewers. Work below ground on the provision, improvement or maintenance of sewers does not require specific planning permission; and the authorities may compulsorily acquire the land for their operations.

"Telecommunications" include systems for the conveyance of speech, music and sounds or visual images and are currently the responsibility of British Telecom under the British Telecommunications Act 1981. Modern techniques of fibre optics and co-axial cable transmission of signals will have a major impact on present systems and methods. British Telecom may place and maintain a telegraph and posts in private land. If the owner fails to give consent for entry a court ruling may be obtained. Privatisation is likely to produce profound changes in the industry.

128

The Pipelines Act 1962 can enable those wishing to construct pipelines to do so without a private act; and the Secretary of State may authorise the compulsory purchase of land by a person proposing to lay a pipeline. There are now a wide variety of pipelines laid transmitting - for example - cement, oil, brine and gases.

In addition to public utilities' apparatus which will have been laid or installed under specific Acts, there may be other apparatus laid by landowners or by others, with the landowners' consent. This could include, for example, television relay cables, private telephone cables, district heating pipes, drains and water services.

IDENTIFICATION OF EXISTING APPARATUS

Most apparatus in urban or developed areas will have been laid along routes defined by road and street systems. In rural or undeveloped areas, apparatus will have been laid predominantly through private land, usually by negotiation and occasionally by compulsory powers. All such transactions should be covered by wayleaves, easements, servitudes, licences and so on and be recorded by the owners of the apparatus and on ownership deeds. It should be noted, however, that records can be inadequate both in respect of the presence of apparatus and its location.

When land is initially assessed for development, the assumption should be made that the site is affected to some degree by public utilities or other apparatus. A visual inspection should be carried out in order to identify any obvious features and all public utilities and any other known owner of apparatus contacted. The enquiry should be accompanied by the most accurate plan available and give details of the use for which the land is being considered. A return date should be stated together with a contact name from whom additional information can be obtained.

Quality of response will depend almost entirely on the detail provided in the enquiry. It should be borne in mind that the accuracy of records is not guaranteed and where necessary the indicated location should be checked on site and verified by means of locators or trial holes.

IMPLICATIONS OF DIVERSION OR ALTERATION

Existing apparatus will have a fundamental effect on the assessment of the site, and in the case of a major obstruction may be the critical factor in the site's selection. From the information received it should be possible to assess the degree to which development will be affected and - after thorough discussion with the public utility concerned - to determine what courses of action can be taken. There are several means of dealing with major obstructions, the following being the most important.

Total or partial diversion can be considered, bearing in mind that considerable cost can be involved, both in terms of physical work and disruption to the system. Simple solutions, seemingly obvious to the developer, often involve complications known only to the specialist who must be given adequate information to form a judgement. An equally important factor is the time-scale required for locating alternative routes [if they exist], negotiating wayleaves, obtaining planning clearances, purchasing specialist materials and so on.

The area of site affected by major apparatus, taking into account safety corridors, could be left undeveloped or not purchased. The loss of developable land might be compensated for by avoiding costly alterations to the apparatus which could be further compounded by delays to the development while apparatus is altered.

The site layout could be organised so that the apparatus has the minimum effect. Obstructions might thus remain unaffected if located within a road verge or under parking or landscaped areas. Major apparatus may require, however, considerable safety corridors within which development cannot take place as well as significant vertical clearances restricting changes in site levels.

If it is determined that site development will proceed, having taken into account the cost of diversion or alteration, it is imperative that the public utility concerned is authorised to proceed as soon as possible. Experience indicates that diversion or alteration procedures are prolonged and often extend beyond the programme time.

Such delays can have severe contractual implications for the developer when other work programmes are affected. The legal priority of a public utility is to maintain public supply and to respond to emergency works. Public utilities will not, therefore, contract with a developer to alter or provide apparatus to an agreed programme. It follows that the co-ordination of works involving public utilities requires special attention in order to avoid delays.

PROVISION OF PUBLIC UTILITIES

Public utilities mains and some services are normally installed in conjunction with site development works to achieve the shortest overall construction period, efficient location of the apparatus and minimisation of future disruption to finishes. The assessment of demand at an early stage is straightforward if the intended building development is bespoke with known details of process requirements and employee numbers.

Where it is intended to provide speculative units, however, assumptions must be made of a generalised nature. The level of provision has to be set so that a balance is achieved between under- and over-provision. Over-provision is uneconomic while under-provision may lead to commercial problems with sale or lease, or subsequent cost and disruption if reinforcement of the system is needed.

Changing economic, employment and production patterns have resulted in substantial changes in demand for services. On modern estates, previously accepted levels for electricity, gas and water now seem high but the advance of modern technology indicates that the requirement for telecommunication facilities will increase.

These changes have been brought about by substantial increases in charges for electricity, gas and water leading to more economic usage; permanent changes in industrial production following loss of traditional heavy industry; and decreasing employment density. Reasons such as automation, improved efficiency and the loss of labour-intensive processes may be quoted. It should be mentioned, however, that desk top assembly processes can result in increased demand for electricity in particular.

Speculatively built factories tend to accommodate lighter industrial processes which are less dependent on prime energy.

When calculating consumption levels for speculative development, developers and public utilities use widely different criteria upon which to base their estimates. It is recommended that a common base is established which will enable consumption to be calculated with uniformity and which enables comparisons to be made between developments.

It is suggested that factory floor area should provide the basis for consumption calculations for the provision of electricity, gas, water and telecommunications. Foul and surface water discharge will be partly a factor of floor area but are also related to other factors.

ESTIMATION OF CONSUMPTION LEVELS

Modern industrial development produces floor areas ranging from 30% to 50% of developable site area. The density will depend upon the size and shape of site, the size and nature of the units and the commercial aims. Densities approaching the lower limit would be found on small sites which provide starter type units or which seek to provide a park environment. The 50% figure is rarely achieved particularly with the trend towards improved environmental standards but the construction of units for high technology, on two or more floors, could lead to high densities. It must be stressed, however, that the developer must estimate the development density, user and employment to provide public utilities with the best information available, based on his experience. It is unreasonable to expect the public utility to do this.

There has been little research carried out into levels of consumption on commercial and industrial estates. Public utilities have indicated that present assumptions, based on experience, are reasonable and that little additional information would be gained from research.

Discussions with public utilities revealed problems in obtaining reliable information from a survey of individual estates.

- Electricity, gas and water require summation of individual meter readings over a protracted period when other factors such as employment levels can significantly alter

- British Telecom research has not identified a clear link between unit size and number of lines required

- Average consumption figures do not relate directly to peak loads.

Research within the development agencies and with public utilities has, however, resulted in the collation of the following information for guidance.

Electricity

Present assumed levels for electricity supply are in the region of 15kVA/100sq m of floor area. It seems acceptable, however, to reduce to 10kVA/100sq m as a general basis as on some large estates average consumption as low as 5kVA/100sq m is not uncommon. The low level of average consumption could be applied when the end use of the development indicates that demand will be low, such as in small workshops or craft units.

The minimum service cable size provided is 25sq mm and will provide a 50kVA three phase supply. On this basis units up to 500sq m floor area can be serviced from the minimum size of service cable. It is recommended that a three phase supply should be provided even to the smallest unit, unless costs are prohibitive.

Heavy industrial users might be served independent of the estate system, direct from a high voltage supply. Within the estate system, substations are normally required to deal with supplies in excess of 150kVA. It is important to reserve sites for substations to deal with future growth.

The advent of computer related technology, particularly when concentrated in science or technology parks, raises problems of stable supply. In rural areas where the supply is predominantly overhead, disruption or fluctuation is more likely taking into account the effects of weather or accidental damage. If new overhead lines are proposed to link the site to the main system, the additional cost of alternative underground cable routes should be considered.

The cost of mains and associated apparatus is charged to the developer on the basis of cost and assessed income.

Gas

Most gas now supplied is natural gas, with very few sources of 'town' gas. Sites which cannot be linked to the gas grid can be provided with liquid petroleum gas [LPG] from individual or communal tanks. The majority of gas used on modern industrial estates is for heating purposes with relatively little process gas. Analysis of supply figures indicates that 1 therm/hour/100sq m of floor area is adequate for heating purposes and allows, in addition, for small process usage.

The reliability of gas supply cannot be assured although local problems can be minimised by the installation of a ring main system. This provision is rare and expensive. Even in this situation there would be no automatic changeover to an alternative source of supply and the critical consumer would have to install his own LPG storage and change over apparatus. An individual high level consumer can make an agreement with the gas authority for an interruptable supply. At times of high national demand the authority may cut off the individual supply for so many days having given the agreed notice. The advantage of the reduced tariff must be assessed against inconvenience and the capital cost of alternative standby plant and fuel.

The cost of mains, services and associated works is recovered from the developer or consumer by gas boards on the basis of cost and assessed income.

Water

Estimates for water supply vary considerably, being mainly caused by different estimates of process water consumption. Sites may be classified as "dry" [light industry and warehousing]; "medium" [light industry with limited process water]; and "wet" [large users of process water]. The variation in range of demand can be by a factor of five to 10.

On speculative development providing light industrial units, classified as "medium" a standard of 1500 litres/eight hour working day/100sq m of floor area is suggested. Lower levels, when domestic water only is provided, are possible but are related to employment levels. Allowance must be made for fire fighting purposes.

Twenty-four hour water storage is often required by the water authority. This storage and closed main circuits can assist in maintaining a continuous supply although this is not guaranteed. An alternative is to extract water from natural sources which requires a statutory licence except in Scotland where extraction is subject only to private legal agreements.

The cost of mains is charged to the developer as a capital cost or a consumption based payment.

Telecomunications

These are presently subject to rapid technological change and the problems of privatisation. Little information exists on desirable provision levels but the usual estate duct system provides capacity well beyond normal needs. In the same way, the minimum service duct size entering a factory has more than adequate capacity.

Reliability of supply cannot be ordinarily guaranteed although cables can be uprated for uses such as the increasing demand for data transmission.

The normal practice for charges is for the developer to install, at his cost, ducts and joint boxes provided free by British Telecom. The main cabling is installed without charge.

Sewers

Design standards for foul and surface water sewers are discussed in the drainage chapter.

In general, other services which may be required are specific to individual units. Alternative heating fuels such as LPG, coal or oil are normally delivered direct to each factory and stored within its own external area. There are instances, however, where units are provided with fuel on a communal basis served by pipe and meter from a bulk supply.

All speculative development must strike a balance between a reasonable level of supply and the cost to the developer of the apparatus installed. The guidance levels of provision given above apply to development where high level users are not anticipated and reasonably low levels of process consumption are expected. On the assumption that these levels only are to be provided it may be prudent, particularly on larger estates, to make provision in the layout for future reinforcement of the estate network.

It is essential to ensure that there is not a too early take up in supply by a high level user which could prejudice the overall development unless there are adequate safeguards.

THE LAYOUT OF MAINS AND SERVICES

The development of new industrial estates offers the opportunity to provide adequate space for the orderly location of the complex array of mains, services, sewers and ducts. These are invariably laid underground, with overhead electricity or telephone cables restricted to isolated or rural sites. In general terms, it is usual to locate this apparatus along the routes of access roads, from which spur connections can be readily taken to buildings. Ducts or road

crossings should be provided at intervals to accommodate future
service connections, without disturbing the highway.

Apparatus should be laid out in a regular and orderly manner so that
individual public utilities can lay, repair and renew their equipment
in safety with minimum disruption to adjacent apparatus and to the
overlying surface. Most public utilities stipulate that their
apparatus should be located in land which will be retained as public
highway and thus not subject to private wayleaves or the like. This
may be logical but has led to the laying of services under
carriageways with consequent problems of settlement, traffic hazard
during repair or connection, and unsightly expensive reinstatement.
Although each public utility must satisfy different criteria, it is
recommended that carriageways should not be used for the location of
apparatus, except where duct or service crossings must be provided.
It is further recommended that sewers should be laid separate from
other apparatus, preferably in the opposite verge of the carriageway
to avoid congestion.

Reserves for apparatus of not less than 2m and preferably 3m wide
should be maintained on both sides of the carriageway, providing level
areas for the construction of footpaths or verges. Where landscape
considerations require ground moulding on service routes it is
imperative that levels are established in advance of the installation
of mains and services. Planting adjacent to verge areas requires
careful design to avoid problems with root growth and the need to
reach underground apparatus in the future. Mains laid in advance of
building access points should be designed to accommodate any
additional loading or change in level.

The layout of apparatus shown in Fig. 16 is recommended for use on
industrial and commercial estates. Other published apparatus layouts
are not designed for industrial use and the recommended layout takes
account of the special requirements of industry and commerce.

Common trenches for services are generally impractical due to
different timing of installation and levels required by each public
utility.

Normal electricity installations involve the laying of high and low
voltage cables, with the low voltage cables feeding individual
buildings. On large sites, or where existing cables have been
diverted, high voltage cables might be encountered. Although
electricity cables are relatively flexible, some cables are
substantial, and although ducted road crossings may be provided,
considerable space for leading in and jointing will be required.
Electricity boards are reluctant to lay any cable which cannot be
energised, because damage to dead cables goes unnoticed until such
time as power is put through them.

Gas mains and services can be laid to limited curves and normally
parallel to kerb lines. Valve or blow out chambers should be

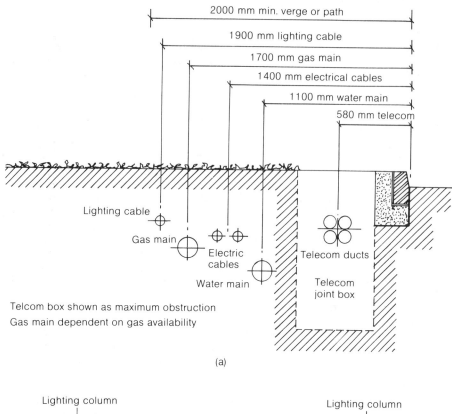

(a)

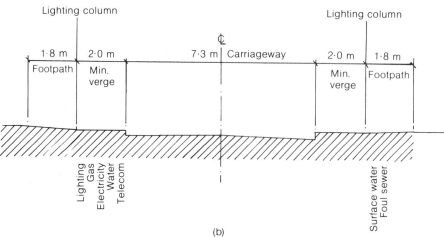

(b)

Fig. 16. Public utilities layout: (a) typical section through footpath and verge; (b) typical section through carriageway, footpath and verges

carefully located to avoid congested areas. Road crossings are required to be gassed up when laid.

Water pipes are laid at sufficient depth to avoid frost damage, normally deeper than other apparatus. Often ducted crossings are provided in advance through which service pipes can be drawn when required.

Telecommunication cables are laid in shallow ducts, leading into joint boxes. The empty ducts, joint boxes and ducted road crossings are installed at an early stage with cabling following when required. Adequate space when laying cables and pipes must be left for joint boxes.

Foul and surface water sewers should be laid parallel wherever possible, and located alongside the carriageway in highway land, separate from other services. Spur connections should be provided and extended to the opposite side of the carriageway, beyond the footpath, verge or other apparatus and terminate in manholes or inspection chambers. Sewers should be laid at sufficient depth to allow the deepest public utilities apparatus to pass over and to allow future connections to be made to the sewer without affecting other apparatus. This requires a minimum depth of cover of 1.2m.

Street lighting cables are laid shallow and at a similar level to telecommunication ducts. It is recommended that lighting columns should be located at the back of footpaths or verges together with their cables. This minimises a hazard to traffic and allows for safer maintenance.

Ducts and road crossings have been previously mentioned but there are general points which should be considered. The object of providing crossings as part of advance works is to eliminate or minimise subsequent excavation in finished construction. Provision should be generous wherever possible but groups of ducts should be avoided to prevent congestion at junction positions. Crossings should be terminated where future connections will cause least intrusion, bearing in mind the physical problems of connecting pipes and cables in footpaths or verges. Ducts should be provided with draw wires attached to markers.

Ducts and crossings must be capable of location in the future, particularly when constructed in advance of building operations. Markers must be permanent and capable of location even when damage may have been caused by construction traffic. This can be achieved by the use of concreted posts or pins, road nails in the road surface, saw cut kerbs or the use of double kerbs laid back-to-back. Accurate as-constructed drawings are essential with duct and crossing positions related by site measurement to permanent adjacent features such as gulleys or manholes.

It is imperative, regardless of layout or method of installation, to ensure that the public utilities work is thoroughly co-ordinated, checked and recorded. Frequent meetings between the developer, contractor and public utilities are essential if the work is to proceed smoothly and problems identified in good time. If the planned layout, location or route of services is amended it is important that the change is made known to other members of the design team. Failure to do this may result in such problems as planting over services, unacceptable variations in cover or the unplanned location of services in unadoptable areas.

Chapter 11

DRAINAGE

INTRODUCTION

The development of an estate requires a drainage system to convey all effluents to outfall points. This takes the form of separate systems for foul, surface water and possibly land drainage. Where separate systems are to connect to a combined sewer they should be interconnected immediately before the outfall point.

The foul water system collects and conveys effluent from buildings, including "domestic" flows from toilets and canteens and "trade" effluent from production processes. The surface water system collects and conveys rainwater from impermeable areas such as roads, yards and roofs together with subsoil water which has percolated through into a land drainage system. The land drainage system may, in some cases, be dealt with independently and connect to a separate outfall.

Simple systems involving cesspits or septic tanks are rare and the majority of projects require a complex pipe and manhole system to dispose of flows generated by the development.

Design standards for drainage systems are not dealt with in detail in this document. There are already in existence adequate reference sources, in particular, the "Standard specification for water and sewerage schemes" issued by the Scottish Development Department / Department of the Environment for Northern Ireland; "Civil engineering specification for the Water Industry" and "Sewers for adoption" issued by the Water Authorities Association.

The more practical implications of alternative drainage systems related to site development are included, however, with particular reference to cost and programme implications of offsite work which can cause the greatest delay.

THE OUTFALL SYSTEM

It is usually the problems associated with the available outfall system which impose limitations on the design of sewers. Where the outfall system is controlled by a sewerage authority or other parties, the developer is immediately faced with the need to negotiate terms which might limit its development, involve a premium for connection or a contribution to improvements. Even in cases where there are no physical limitations on connection, there could be delays in finalising consents, wayleaves and so on. In more complex situations where the outfall system is inadequate in terms of condition, capacity or effluent standards, the developer must consider what alternatives provide the most effective solution. It is important to assess the realistic cost and time-scale of offsite works, particularly when such works would be carried out by others and recharged to the developer who may in turn have little control over the construction programme.

Where limitations exist in the foul water system to which the site should connect, or where no outfall system exists, the developer will have to assess the added cost and complications of treatment on site. The balance between the installation and running costs of onsite treatment plant and sewerage charges requires thorough investigation as a favourable rate of return on the initial capital investment can be obtained in certain cases.

An alternative method of limiting foul water discharge in unacceptable periods is to provide onsite storage. Flows may be retained onsite at peak periods and discharged by pumps or valved outlets at off peak periods when the flow or effluent standard is acceptable.

Surface water storm peaks can be retained by storage in balancing reservoirs, which can be constructed underground as formal structures or using large diameter pipes. An often cheaper alternative is the formation of balancing lakes which can be used to good effect as unique landscape features, although this involves the sterilisation of land which could otherwise have been available for some commercial purpose. The incorporation of any water retaining structure must, however, be treated with caution as public safety may require statutory involvement under the appropriate Act with onerous inspection and maintenance procedures in perpetuity. The effect of varying water levels on existing or proposed vegetation should be assessed.

A comparatively recent innovation is the use of hydrobrakes on surface water or combined systems. Outfall flows are restricted to a predetermined level by causing turbulance within piped systems. The reduction in flow is achieved by using the upstream storage capacity of the pipe and manhole system.

If onsite restrictions on discharge are not practical or economic, the offsite system may require improvement, or where no convenient outfall exists a new system may lead to improvements at the developer's expense or at a cost shared with other parties. In situations where an entirely new system must be installed, the developer may negotiate for the system to be installed under its control or may requisition the system from the sewerage authority or its agents.

REQUISITIONS

When offsite sewers must be laid on land not in the ownership or control of the developer, arrangements must be made for laying pipes within that land. This can either be done by mutual agreement or requesting the sewerage authority to apply its statutory powers. The conditions for requisitioning a sewer vary throughout the United Kingdom and early discussion with the sewerage authority is essential. For example, requisitions may only be undertaken in England and Wales for "domestic" drainage under Section 16 of the Water Act 1973 whereas in Scotland all types of drainage can be catered for under the Sewerage [Scotland] Act 1968 Section two.

The sewerage authority has a responsibility to provide sewers for an area and the developer may request such sewers to be provided. However, he will find that in many cases he will be required to make a contribution towards the provision of such sewers. In England and Wales this is based on the extra-over cost of providing the sewer for "domestic" effluent only. In Scotland the sewerage authority determines a reasonable cost and the developer is required to pay the balance. These charges can either be paid as a lump sum or over a 12 year period with some relief by the sewerage authority depending on the rate income available.

Authorities are reluctant to provide pumping stations on the grounds of perpetual maintenance and running costs. Where pumping cannot be avoided, the developer is normally required to provide the station as part of his on site drainage system rather than an integral part of the requisitioned sewer. The merits of providing such a pumping station have to be balanced against the possibility of adoption and the perpetual running costs to the developer.

The developer must take account of any delay which these procedures [including negotiations for rights of way and land] might cause to the development of the site. It must carefully relate the implications of delay against any other alternatives.

ADOPTION

An essential consideration in the design and construction of sewers is that the completed system should be suitable for adoption by the sewerage authority under the terms of the relevant Act. There might be circumstances where the developer would not seek adoption such as where it wishes to retain control over the sewers or where adoption standards impose unacceptably high costs. Adoption standards are not normally excessive and reflect accepted good practice. It should also be borne in mind that an unadopted system might lead to increased costs of maintenance and repair, for which the developer would be responsible; and prejudice the extension of such a system in the future. This could have an impact on any commercial dealings at a later stage.

It is desirable that the developer and the sewerage authority enter an agreement under the relevant act that the sewers will be adopted on completion if constructed to agreed design and construction standards. The agreement is subject to supervision of work by the authority. The cost of supervision might possibly be recharged to the developer at around 2.5% of the scheme cost. Alternatively there is provision for sewers to be offered for adoption after completion. As the design and construction standards will not have been agreed, the authority may insist on rigorous investigation of the system, including the provision of full design information.

Agreements require that sewers and other works for adoption are constructed in the developer's land. In other cases the authority would have to be satisfied as to the transfer of ownership or the creation of rights necessary for its purposes in relation to any pumping station site and the developer's entitlement to transfer rights in respect of offsite sewers. The developer is required to obtain all necessary statutory consents, particularly with respect to all landowners affected, the highway authority, and public utilities. A performance bond equal to 10% of the agreed estimated cost can be required, the bond being released after the works have been vested in the authority.

Adoption procedures require time and this factor should be included in the development programme as delays can be expensive.

FOUL SEWERS

The foul water system is designed to collect and convey flows of contaminated water from toilets, canteens and trade processes to an outfall point, preferably by gravity. The flow from toilets and canteens is classified as "domestic" effluent and is directly related to employment level. The flow from trade processes is known as "trade" effluent and varies substantially in volume and quality. On modern industrial estates, with a majority of small units, flows are predominantly domestic with relatively little trade effluent by volume, although the nature of the effluent can be extremely variable. Modern high technology processes, even in small premises, can produce toxic effluents associated, for example, with the production of printed circuits.

Where bespoke development is to follow sewer construction, a high level of design information will be available for the calculation of flows and the assessment of composition. Where, however, the development is speculative there will be little information available and a more general assessment must be made.

It is reasonable to assume in calculating design flows that a correctly designed and constructed system will not be subject to significant infiltration by ground water. Flows should equate reasonably to water consumption although peaks of supply and discharge will not necessarily relate. Analysis of development agency criteria

for foul water sewer design indicates that factory floor area is
seldom used as a basis for design. The most common design basis is
site area giving a figure of 1 litre/sec/ha [1 cumin/acre] for
"medium" flows. Restricted water supply or limitations on outfall
capacity may well determine the total flow from an estate and limit
factory use to "dry floor" processes.

Even when total flows are small it is not recommended that any gravity
sewer or pipe be less than 150mm diameter, as any lesser size is not
likely to be adopted and prone to blockage. Care is required to avoid
infiltration into the sewer system by means of good design and
construction practice at all stages of the development. Excessive
infiltration increases the cost of pumping or treatment and might
render the sewer unadoptable. The adoption standard for infiltration
into pipelines and manholes requires that in 30 minutes infiltration
does not exceed 0.5 litre per lineal metre per metre of nominal bore
size.

SURFACE WATER SEWERS

The surface water system is designed to collect and convey all
rainwater falling onto impermeable areas, for an assumed frequency of
storm, together with a proportion of subsoil water collected by a land
drainage system.

There are a number of methods of calculating surface water flow and
the most up to date method is the "Design and analysis of urban storm
drainage - the wallingford procedure" published by the Department of
the Environment. This report covers efficient and cost-effective
drainage of urban areas using computer based methods. The
Lloyd-Davies or TRRL Hydrograph methods can be used for small sites.

The following factors form the normal basis of hydraulic design:

- Storm frequency of two years and approximately 50mm/hour rainfall
- Time of entry - normally three minutes
- Impermeability for industrial development of approximately 70%.

These factors require analysis for each specific site.

Where surface water can be contaminated by fuel and oil droppings from
vehicles in parking and service areas, interceptor chambers should be
provided to prevent this contamination passing through the system into
water courses. It has been found that the provision of an interceptor
to each unit is uneconomical. Interceptors which serve a group of
units or a whole estate are more economic but can be subject to
difficulties with the sewerage authorities in terms of public
adoption. Many authorities are reluctant to adopt such interceptors
and the developer will have to provide an efficient maintenance
service if such interceptor systems are installed.

Consent will be required to discharge a surface water system into a

143

water course either from a river purification board in Scotland or a water authority in England, Wales and Northern Ireland. Certain standards will be imposed regarding the construction of the outfall and the standard of water being discharged into the water course. Safety precautions will be required at the intake and outfall points to prevent unauthorised entry to the systems. It is also necessary to strike a balance on the interception and retention of debris with the degree of maintenance and clearance that will be provided.

LAND DRAINAGE

Land which has a history of cultivation is likely to have a significant system of land drainage. This will involve an irregular pattern of drains ranging from disused to functioning runs. When new development disrupts live systems it is important that the broken runs are reinstated or diverted into the new drainage system as quickly as possible. If this is not done, waterlogging of ground and reduction in bearing capacity can occur.

When advance preparation works are undertaken, any adjustment of the land drainage system should allow for subsequent building operations and land drainage around building plots if possible. It should be noted that the alterations of existing systems or the installation of new land drains will affect the balance of ground water over the site, which may have a detrimental effect on vegetation. The location of new drains should be known to the landscape architect.

The design of new land drainage works must ensure that the drain's effectiveness is not seriously affected by subsequent development of the site. Incorrect design can lead to the rapid silting of filter drains or the blockage of filter stone by topsoil or turf. Even routine maintenance operations such as grass cutting can block filter layers as cuttings are deposited or washed over the drain. Open ditches or culverts require maintenance to keep profiles free from washed down materials and plant growth.

Land drains may be laid in a variety of materials including clay, concrete, pitch fibre or plastics. The type of pipe and filter layer will be determined by the funtion of the drain including whether it is intended to intercept ground water or water flowing over the ground surface. Geotextiles may be used to prevent the migration of fines into the drainage layer. The type and grading of filter stone will depend upon soil conditions and the function of the drain, but careful thought must be given to the surface layer at ground level to reduce vandalism.

Catch pits and sumps should be located at the junction between land drains and surface water drains as well as along their length to allow proper maintenance, and be generously proportioned. When determining the levels of land drains, particularly at the point of entry to a system, account must be taken of surcharge levels within the sewer.

Advance preparation works can be limited to the provision of access roads and associated earthworks without the levelling of sites for building development. Alternatively, site development may involve the establishing of final levels over the whole site in a comprehensive earthworks operation. Whenever large areas of land are stripped of topsoil, and subsoil in its natural or disturbed state is left exposed, the erosion of soil or the deterioration of soil conditions must be assessed. Ground levels should maintain a nominal fall of approximately 1% to prevent ponding.

When a site is assessed for development, particularly when the development is long-term, the provision of advance land drainage should be considered as a method of ground improvement. The installation of cut-off drains to reduce flows of ground water, or deep drains to lower the water table substantially could result in improvement which more than covers the cost of drainage.

The design and specification of field drainage systems is covered by various publications issued by the Agricultural Development & Advisory Service [ADAS] of the Ministry of Agriculture, Fisheries and Food. The main publications are "The design of field drainage pipe systems" and "Technical note on workmanship and materials for field drainage schemes". Although these are related to agriculture they provide useful guidance to designers.

GENERAL STANDARDS FOR DESIGN AND CONSTRUCTION

As mentioned previously it is recommended that sewers are constructed to the standards required for adoption by the sewerage authority. However, there are some general points which are recommended to be included in the design of a separate system.

Sewers should be located adjacent to highways under footpaths or verges and on the opposite side of the carriageway from public utilities apparatus. Manholes should not be located where they can obstruct other public utilities.

Maximum manhole spacing should not exceed 100m. The size of the manhole should be adequate to cater for safe access and egress, operatives to work, and the accommodation of channels and benching at the base. Blank connections should be provided in manhole bases to avoid serious disruption in the future. Blank connections should be over-sized so that the incoming pipe can be sleeved through the connection and grouted in. Until brought into use blank connections should be fitted with permanent stoppers. Deep manholes require special provision for safety. Safety in sewers is covered by "Safe working in sewers and sewage works" published by the National Joint Health & Safety Committee for the Water Service.

Sewer levels should maintain a minimum cover of 1.2m where conflict with public utilities apparatus is likely. In other areas they should be deep enough to avoid land drains and never laid at less than 0.9m cover. Where sewers are laid parallel the relative level of foul and surface water sewers should allow for side connections. It is recommended that the foul sewer is laid deeper than the surface water sewer to allow foul water connections to pass beneath; the surface water sewer being generally of larger diameter than the foul.

Minimum velocity of flow should not be less than 1m/second at full bore so that partial flow velocity exceeds 0.75m/second.

Flexible joints are generally recommended for pipes and connections to manholes together with adequately designed bedding and backfill to accommodate likely loads on the pipelines. Particular attention should be paid to water tightness of manholes and pipe joints to prevent infiltration.

PUMPED SYSTEMS

Pumping stations are expensive to provide, operate and maintain and can cause septicity and noise problems. They should only be considered when a gravity system is impracticable or uneconomic to provide, as already mentioned. Where there is no alternative, the pumping of foul sewage is normally straightforward as the relatively low volumes and even flow rates allow limited storage and a simple pump installation. The pumping of surface water, or of foul sewage diluted by high levels of ground water through infiltration is more complex. The flows to be pumped fluctuate, requiring extensive storage and specialised equipment.

The location of a pumping station will depend upon the layout of the gravity system feeding to it, the position of the outfall point and the route available for the rising main. Reasonable facilities for vehicular access must be available to allow repair and maintenance, including transporting the largest item of plant which may have to be replaced. A three phase electricity power supply will be needed and the station may require a telemetry link and mains water for washing down. Although most sumps and pump wells are underground there will be items above ground which might influence the location of the station to limit intrusion.

A minimum of two pumps should be provided, one duty and one standby of the same capacity. Where two or more duty pumps are provided of differing capacity, the standby pump should be equal to the capacity of the larger duty pump. Pumps and motors must be capable of replacement without undue difficulty and the removal of one unit should not influence the working of the standby plant. To cope with power failure the station should allow for the convenient location of a mobile generator and facilities should be provided for the connection of temporary cables. Consideration should be given to methods of dealing with emergency overflows.

The design of rising mains should ensure that velocities of flow are

146

between 0.75m/sec and 1.8m/sec. The rising main should be as short as possible. Changes of direction should be anchored and the pipe provided with air release valves at summits and washouts at low points. Where future access is likely to cause major disruption, the duplication of the main should be considered together with isolation valves. Unless otherwise defined, the route should be indicated by permanent markers.

REFERENCES AND FURTHER READING

AGRICULTURAL DEPARTMENT AND ADVISORY SERVICE (ADAS) OF THE MINISTRY OF AGRICULTURE, FISHERIES AND FOOD. The Design of field drainage pipe systems. 1982.

AGRICULTURAL DEPARTMENT AND ADVISORY SERVICE (ADAS) OF THE MINISTRY OF AGRICULTURE, FISHERIES AND FOOD. Technical note on workmanship and materials for field drainage schemes. 1983, May.

NATIONAL JOINT HEALTH AND SAFETY COMMITTEE FOR THE WATER SERVICE. Safe working in sewers and sewage works. 1979, November.

SCOTTISH DEVELOPMENT DEPARTMENT. Standard Specification for Water and Sewerage Schemes. HMSO Edinburgh, 1979.

WATER AUTHORITIES ASSOCIATION. Civil engineering specification for the water industry. Water Research Centre on behalf of Water Authorities. 1984.

WATER AUTHORITIES ASSOCIATION. Sewers for Adoption. Water Research Centre on behalf of Water Authorities Association. 1985.

IMPLEMENTATION

Chapter 12

ADVANCE PREPARATION OF SITE INFRASTRUCTURES

INTRODUCTION

In the overall planning of site development works, consideration must be given to the extent of items which should be completed in advance of the letting of any building contract. There is also the option to combine the constructions of infrastructure and buildings under one contract but very much depends on the relative extent and content of the two types of work and the proportion of the site which will be involved in the initial building programme.

In the first instance, a detailed development programme must be prepared and discussed with the developer in order to obtain its approval. This programming process should identify the elements of site development which can or should be carried out under separate contracts from the buildings. By way of illustration three main categories can be considered.

WORK NECESSARY BEFORE ANY BUILDING CAN PROCEED

The policy of the developer may dictate the extent of completion of infrastructure prior to any building contract. In addition there are technical consideratons which may influence this decision for it can be administratively easier and more economic to employ specialist subcontractors direct rather than as subcontractors to the main contactor. Ground engineering can fall into this category - with distinct predevelopment contracts for ground improvement techniques such as dynamic compaction and preloading. Extensive earthworks involving major infill are most economic when completed in one contract even though drainage, roads and other infrastructural items might be phased over a number of contracts or years. The highway authority may require that site access from a heavy trafficked road should be completed prior to start of construction operations as an aid to road safety.

WORK NECESSARY BEFORE BUILDINGS CAN BE OCCUPIED

The minimum requirements of a building occupier are adequate road access, main drainage both on and off site and public utilities. The extent of this work linked to building contracts will depend on the wishes of the developer. However, most enlightened developers would wish to have estate roads and main drainage substantially completed

along with regrading and structure landscaping in advance of
building.

If roads are constructed in advance a case can sometimes be made out
for the omission of the wearing course from roads or flexible
construction until after completion of the buildings. Such an
omission is known to increase overall costs and proper forward
planning with the supply of road crossings and ducts can avoid damage
to the finished surface. On the other hand it is not normally
practical to complete footpaths and verges until such time as all the
public utilities have been laid. Although some public utilities will
be laid in advance of specific requirements, others will not be laid
until there is a consumer, and this can involve a protracted period
of time. In any event the verges should be dressed off and even
grassed so as not to give an unfinished appearance to the
infrastructure.

ALL OTHER ITEMS WHICH WILL AFFECT THE PROGRESS OF DEVELOPMENT

Programming of all work on a site is not entirely in the hands of the
developer and a schedule of such work should be prepared at an early
stage. This type of work may involve diversion of public footpaths,
utilities or private services. In adddition, although the developer
may own the land, legal requirements, such as the termination of an
agricultrual tenancy, may constrain the programme of development.

This programme must be based on realistic assessment of the
requirements of the public utilities and allow sufficient time for the
negotiation of wayleaves. This is particularly important when the
development calls for the provision of offsite drainage through land
in the ownership of others who can impose conditions on the programme
of laying. Public utilities have an obligation to deal with
emergencies as they arise and therefore there can be further programme
disruption.

Most local authorities are eager to advance developments within their
area but no developer should assume that their particular project is
the only one that is taking place. Adequate time must therefore be
built into the programme to ensure that full discussions can take
place and formal approvals issued.

Site development works can only be carried out at a time to suit the
developer's cash flow, or budget allocations in the cases of
developers in the public sector. The phasing of the work to suit the
proposed building or land sale programme has the greatest impact on
the site development programme, for if the initial intention is to
open up only a small part of the site it is clearly not necessary to
construct the whole of the infrastructure in the first instance, and
flexibility of later developments can be seriously affected by early
over-provision. The technical team must be made fully aware of the
availablility of finance in order that this can be taken into account
when considering the programme of works.

Finally, there are the marketing considerations of the developer to be taken into account. Few developers would wish to proceed unless they can be sure that the site development works will improve the overall appearance of the estate at an early stage so as to give an insight into how it will appear when fully developed. Hence structure landscaping should be carried out as part of the initial phase of site preparation together with any demolition of buildings and land clearance in order to achieve this objective. Care should be taken to finish off the whole area in a neat and tidy fashion. It is likely that landscaping will be carried out as a separate contract to suit the planting season.

IMPLEMENTATION

Infrastructure and building works are normally carried out by two different types of contractor. If the developer imposes a short time-scale on the overall development then the merits of either a combined contract or separate concurrent contracts have to be considered.

It is advisable to employ the same consultants for both sections of the work in order to avoid conflicting designs.

In many locations it is not easy to prepare an adequate tender list of contractors equally suitable for civil engineering and building. If separate contracts are adopted then the tender documents must ensure that:

- There is no conflict between two or more contractors working within a limited area simultaneously

- Infrastructure elements required to allow the building to proceed are programmed to be complete in order to avoid delay to the building works.

If there are suitable contractors in the area, the advantages of combined contract can be assessed in terms of a short time-scale and cost.

In those few cases where the developments are of a very large nature and several contracts are operating simultaneously, then the developer should consider the appointment of a separate project manager whose duty would be to ensure the avoidance of conflict between the different sections of the work - both design and construction - and the overall maintenance of programme. Such a project manager could be drawn from the technical team, either from a consultancy or an in-house department, or could be an independent specialist.

The basis of the conditions of contract for site development works, including landscaping, is generally the ICE Conditions of Contract.

The technical team should obtain the developer's agreement on the conditions of contract, including variations to suit the project which are proposed for use. Depending on the status of the developer the team must be prepared to give advice on this subject. At the same time procedures required by the developer to obtain and report on tenders must be strictly followed.

The developer may require advice on the obtaining of tenders but it is likely that public sector developers will have definite procedures which must be followed for the invitation and opening of tenders. It is important that the technical team understands these procedures in order to ensure that there is no infringement of them.

MONITORING

Team members must immediately advise developers of any unexpected problems which arise on site which could escalate costs or affect the programme. Similarly, the team is not usually at liberty freely to make use of savings which have been achieved in one section of the work for some elaboration elsewhere. It is now common practice to limit to some extent the powers of the consultants on the technical team to vary the work content at the time of their appointment by the developer. Care is required that such limitations are not self-defeating by preventing the consultants from making considered judgements about items which might have an adverse effect on the contract.

Variations in the programme of individual sections of a contract may occur, and although these may not affect the overall contract completion it is possible that there could be expenditure implications. The developer must be informed of these variations in order that any cash flow proposals can be assessed against actual requirements.

REFERENCES AND FURTHER READING

THE INSTITUTION OF CIVIL ENGINEERS. THE ASSOCIATION OF CONSULTING ENGINEERS. THE FEDERATION OF CIVIL ENGINEERING CONTRACTORS. Conditions of Contract and Forms of Tender, Agreement and Bond for use in connection with Works of Civil Engineering Construction. Fifth Edition (June 1973) (Revised January 1979).

APPENDICES

Appendix One

EXAMPLES A, B AND C

EXAMPLE 'A'

Assume a 10 acre site where preliminary negotiations indicate a purchase price of £90,000. The requirement is to open up developable plots through the construction of a main estate road, drainage, services, and site levelling with limited structural landscaping. Serviced plots will ultimately be disposed of on a freehold basis. Assume construction period of six months.

ESTIMATED TOTAL SITE DEVELOPMENT COSTS

1. **Construction costs**

	£	£
Road/levelling etc costs	200,000	
Other items [substation]	10,000	
Site investigation fees	6,000	
Design etc fees [6.5% on £210,000]	13,650	
Clerk of Works costs	3,000	
Statutory fees	4,000	
		236,650
Internal admin. fees etc [2.5% on £210,000]	5,250	
		5,250

2. **Interest/finance charges [assume 11%]**

	£	£
On land price during construction = £90,000 for six months @ 11%	4,950	
On half construction etc costs during construction [assume constant cash flow over six months] = £118,325 for six months @ 11%	6,508	
On land finance and construction etc, costs prior to disposal of plots. Say £338,108 for six months @ 11%	18,596	
		30,054

3. **Miscellaneous costs**

	£	£
Agents fees for sales etc	4,050	
Advertising	1,000	
		5,050
	TOTAL	£277,004

157

COSTS MUST NOW BE RELATED TO VALUE

Existing Value – 10 acres @ £9,000 per acre =		£90,000
Plus total site development costs	=	£277,004
TOTAL INVESTMENT	=	£367,004
Enhanced value after		
works nine acres @ £45,000	=	£405,000
PROFIT ON DEVELOPMENT	=	£37,996

For a total expenditure of £367,004 a profit of £37,996 would ultimately be achieved, assuming estimates etc did not vary.

EXAMPLE ´B´

Assume a 10 acre site where preliminary negotiations indicate a purchase price
of £25,000. A small workshop scheme of 15,000 sq ft is to be constructed, in
conjunction with certain site development works to render the ground suitable
for development [a site levelling and ground stabilisation exercise is
necessary]. Assume site development/construction period of nine months.

ESTIMATED TOTAL SITE DEVELOPMENT COSTS

				£
1.	Land costs - one acre @ £25,000 [incl fees etc]			25,000

2. Construction/site development costs

	£	
Ground levelling	50,000	
Ground stabilisation	30,000	
Building costs	300,000	
Site investigation fees	2,500	
Design etc fees [6.5% on £380,000]	24,700	
Clerk of Works costs	3,800	
Statutory fees	4,500	
		415,500
Internal admin fees etc		
[2.5% on £380,000]	9,500	9,500

3. Interest/finance charges [assume 11%]

	£	£
On land price during construction		
= £25,000 for nine months @ 11%	2,062	
On half construction etc costs during construction [assume constant cash flow over nine months] = £207,750 for nine months @ 11%	17,139	
On land construction etc and costs prior to units let/sold. Say £459,701 for nine months @ 11%	25,284	
		44,485

4. Miscellaneous costs

	£	£
Agents letting fees	4,350	
Advertising	1,000	
		5,350
	TOTAL	£499 835

COSTS MUST NOW BE RELATED TO ANTICIPATED RENTALS

		£
10 units @ 500 sq ft = 5,000 sq ft @ £3.20/sq ft =		16,000
5 units @ 1,000 sq ft = 5,000 sq ft @ £2.90/sq ft =		14,500
2 units @ 2,500 sq ft = 5,000 sq ft @ £2.60/sq ft =		13,000
	TOTAL	£43,500
Less management fees @ say 3% £1,305		
Landlords repairs £3,480		
		4,785
	Estimated net rents	£38,715

Assuming total development costs of £499,835 and estimated net rents of £38,715
initial return on capital would be 7.7%. This would require checking with
identified development objectives to determine whether appraisal result is
satisfactory, and level of return is acceptable.

EXAMPLE ´C´

Consider again the example given in Annex ´A´ of a 10 acre site to be opened up with estate road, drainage, services, levelling etc. Assume in this instance that the serviced land is <u>not</u> now sold off in developable plots but is to accommodate a first phase of development, comprising 15,000 sq ft of small units on one acre of the 10 acre site. Assume a three-month site development contract and six-month building contract. The remaining land will be held for subsequent development proposals.

ESTIMATED TOTAL SITE DEVELOPMENT COSTS

1. Construction costs

	£	£
Road, levelling etc costs	200,000	
Other items [sub station]	10,000	
Site investigation fees	6,500	
Design etc fees [6.5% on £210,000]	13,650	
Clerk of Works costs	3,000	
Statutory fees	4,500	
		236,650
Internal admin fees etc [2.5% on £380,000]	5,250	5,250

2. Interest/finance charges [assume 11%]

	£	£
On land price during construction = £90,000 for three months @ 11%	2,475	
On half construction etc costs during construction [assume constant cash flow over three months @ 11%]	3,254	
		5,729
TOTAL estimated site development costs		£247,629

TOTAL COSTS SHOULD NOW BE APPORTIONED BETWEEN PHASE ONE DEVELOPMENT AND REMAINDER OF LAND:

Total areas serviced - 10 acres @ cost of £247,629
Amount apportioned to 15,000 sq ft on one acre £24,763

Amount apportioned to remaining nine acres £222,866

Ignoring the one acre taken for Phase one development at this stage, it is now possible to undertake a traditional site development appraisal on the nine acres remaining, eg

	£
Existing value - nine acres @ £9,000/acre	81,000
<u>Apportioned</u> site development costs	222,866
TOTAL INVESTMENT	£303,866
Value after site development works - eight acres @ £45,000/acre	360,000
PROFIT ON DEVELOPMENT	£56,134

This figure of course assumes an immediate realisation of the development value in the fully serviced areas. If it is believed [due to market conditions] the eight acres will only be disposed of on a phased basis then account would need to be taken of interest charges etc. to gain a more realistic impression.

Having calculated an apportionment of the site development works attributable to Phase one development it now remains to include these figures within the normal development appraisal.

PHASE ONE ESTIMATED TOTAL DEVELOPMENT COSTS

		£	£
1.	Land costs - one acre @ £9,000 [incl fees etc]		9,000
2.	Construction etc costs		

	£	£
Building costs	300,000	
Site investigation fees	2,500	
Design etc fees [6.5% on £300,000]	19,500	
Clerk of Works costs	3,000	
Statutory fees	4,500	
Apportioned site development costs	24,763	
		354,263
Internal admin fees etc [2.5% on £300,000]	7,500	7,500

3. Interest/finance charges [assume 11%]
On land price during construction
= £9,000 for six months @ 11%   495

On half construction etc costs
[assume constant cash flow]
= £177,132 for six months @ 11%]   9,742

On lane, construction, finance, etc
costs until units let/sold. Say
£348,056 for six months @ 11%   20,543
                                                              30,780

4. Miscellaneous costs

Agents letting fees   4,350
Advertising   1,000
                                                               5,350

                                            TOTAL   £406,893

COSTS MUST AGAIN BE RELATED TO ANTICIPATED RENTALS

10 units @   500 sq ft = 5,000 sq ft @ £3.20/sq ft =   16,000
 5 units @ 1,000 sq ft = 5,000 sq ft @ £2.90/sq ft =   14,500
 2 units @ 2,500 sq ft = 5,000 sq ft @ £2.60/sq ft =   13,000

                                    TOTAL   £43,500
Less management fees @ say 3% £1,305
Landlords repairs   £3,480
                                                         4,785

                    Estimated net rents   £38,715

Assuming total development costs of £406,893 and estimated net rents of £38,715 INITIAL RETURN ON CAPITAL would be 9.5%.

This would require cross-reference with previously identified development objective to determine whether level of return is acceptable.

Appendix Two

ANALYSIS OF SITE DEVELOPMENT COSTS — METRIC AND IMPERIAL

	Land uses	Percent	Hectares [ha]			
1.1	Net developable area					
1.2	Roads, services, etc					
1.3	Gross site area		100.0			

		£ Percent	£ per ha GSA	£ per ha DPA	£ per sq m GIA/GEA
	Estimated costs				
2.1	Investigation and planning [actual cost]				
2.2	Clearance, earthworks and ground improvement				
2.3	Foul and surface water drainage —off-site —on-site				
2.4	Roads and footpaths				
2.5	Utilities [water, gas, electricity, telecoms] —off-site —on-site				
2.6	Landscape works				
2.7	Signs and street furniture				
2.8	Fees and expenses for items 2.2-2.7	100.0			
2.9	Total site preparation				
2.10	Land acquisition				
2.11	Administration costs				
2.12	Total site development	100.0			

Note   1.   Design and price risk and contingency allowances
              including in items 2.2 and 2.7

        2.   Estimates based on prices current on..................

	Land uses	Percent	Acres [ac]
1.1	Net developable area		
1.2	Roads, services, etc		
1.3	Gross site area	100.0	

	Estimated costs	£ Percent	£ per ac GSA	£ per ac DPA	£ per sq ft GIA/GEA
2.1	Investigation and planning [actual cost]				
2.2	Clearance, earthworks and ground improvement				
2.3	Foul and surface water drainage -off-site -on-site				
2.4	Roads and footpaths				
2.5	Utilities [water, gas, electricity, telecoms] -off-site -on-site				
2.6	Landscape works				
2.7	Signs and street furniture				
2.8	Fees and expenses for items 2.2-2.7	100.0			
2.9	Total site preparation				
2.10	Land acquisition				
2.11	Administration costs				
2.12	Total site development	100.0			

Note   1.   Design and price risk and contingency allowances including in items 2.2 and 2.7

2.   Estimates based on prices current on..................

Appendix Three

GROUND INVESTIGATION TESTS

1] Piezometer - This equipment, consisting basically of a polythene tube with a porous filter at the lower end effectively sealed from the upper part of the borehole by a clay plug, is used to measure the porewater pressure. This is done by measuring the rise of the water level within the polythene tube.

2] Standard penetration test [SPT] - This test is probably the most commonly used in cable percussive work in obtaining preliminary information on ground strength. Basically, the test consists of recording the number of blows of a 63.4 kilos [140 lb] weight free falling 750 mm [30"] it takes to drive a 50mm [2"] diameter tube [spoon] four successive increments of 75 mm [3"] after an initial seating of 150 mm [6"].

3] Pumping tests - These tests are carried out in order to assess the viability of ground water abstraction; a borehole is sunk to water bearing strata and a pumping system set up capable of quantifying a substantial rate flow.

4] The cone penetrometer can be found in mechanical and electrical form.

The mechanical cone is designed to deliver cone point resistance whereas the electrical cone is designed to deliver electrical readouts of cone point resistance and friction of subsurface materials for the identification of soil types.

Verticality can be checked with an inclinometer integrated into the cone. The output data in chart form is used as the primary investigative source material and core boring and sampling are used as supplementary information. It is fair to say that the penetrometer operates best in soft to stiff clay soils. Its applications are the determination of stratigraphy, foundation settlement, estimating shear strengths, pile capacity, compaction control, etc.

The penetrometer contains the necessary load cells and cable connections; one end of the unit is threaded to receive the sounding rods. The hydraulic thrust system is mounted over the centre of gravity of the truck, permitting the use of a full 15 tonne truck weight as a load reaction. The system gives a highly versatile mechanism with a good work output.

Each site must be considered individually, identifying what information is required when selecting which laboratory tests to carry out.

LABORATORY TESTS ON SAMPLES

1] Soil classification test - moisture content, density, plasticity index [liquid limit/plastic limit] specific gravity, particle size distribution.

2] Soil/water chemical tests - total sulphate content, pH value of water sample, water soluble sulphate content of soil, total chloride content, organic content of soil, electrical conductivity.

3] Soil compaction test - moisture content/dry density relationship, [rammer method - BS1377:1975 test 12 & 13; vibrating hammer method BS1377:1975 test 14].

4] Pavement design test - California bearing ratio [CBR].

5] Soil strength test - triaxial compression - unconsolidated/consolidated/drained/undrained, uniaxial compression, direct shear - unconsolidated/consolidated/drained/undrained, tensile strength [rock], California bearing ratio, vane test.

6] Soil deformation tests - consolidation test [Oedemeter BS1377:1975 test 17].

7] Soil permeability test - constant head/falling head permeameter, Packer or Lugeon test [rock].

The preceeding tests are those commonly in use in ground investigation, more specialised tests are listed below for reference:

8] Soil corrosivity test

9] Rock classification test

10] Dynamic test

11] Rock strength test

12] Rock deformation test

13] Rock permeability test

NB Every site must be considered individually, identifying what information is required when selecting which laboratory tests to carry out.